MW00564837

ADVANCE PRAISE FOR *STONE YARD DEVOTIONAL*

A Book of the Year for
the *Sydney Morning Herald* and *ABC*

'A slim novel which tackles weighty themes – guilt,
loss, forgiveness – and manages to be both profound
and addictively entertaining. I loved it'
Clare Chambers, author of *Small Pleasures*

'Beautiful, strange and otherworldly, Charlotte Wood's
latest novel is an absorbing mediation on grief, forgiveness
and our relationship to the natural world'
Paula Hawkins, author of *A Slow Fire Burning*

Stone Yard Devotional shows us the mysteries of human
relationships, asking who can and should bestow forgiveness.
This novel is subtly powerful and utterly engrossing'
Claire Fuller, author of *Unsettled Ground*

'Quiet but weighty, *Stone Yard Devotional* is all about
the complicated task of loving the world and its
creatures. No words can quite convey how much I loved
this book. I am just so happy to have read it'
Karen Joy Fowler, author of *Booth*

'Magnificent and radical . . . It gripped me
from the opening line to the very last'

Age

'A book that extends and deepens Wood's already remarkable
achievements as a novelist in powerful and often profound
ways . . . It is a mark of Wood's sophistication as a writer that
the novel does not attempt to resolve these contradictions.
Instead it suggest that goodness is fraught and imperfect and
that the bonds of love and obligation, kindness and cruelty
that bind us to one another are written deep in our bodies,
shaping us in ways we cannot ever fully escape or understand'

Saturday Paper

PRAISE FOR *THE WEEKEND*

A *Sunday Times* 'Best Book for Summer 2021'

A *Times, Guardian* and *Daily Mail* paperback pick

A *Times, Observer, Independent, Daily Express*
and *Good Housekeeping* Book of the Year

*Winner, 2020 Literary Fiction Book of the
Year, Australian Book Industry Awards*

Shortlisted, 2020 Stella Prize

Shortlisted, 2020 Best Fiction, Indie Awards

Shortlisted, 2020 ALS Gold Medal

*Shortlisted, 2020 Best Fiction, Prime
Minister's Literary Awards*

*Shortlisted, 2021 Christina Stead Prize for
Fiction, NSW Premier's Literary Awards*

'A perfect, funny, insightful novel about
women, friendship and ageing'
Nina Stibbe

'Triumphantly brings to life the honest inner lives of women'
Independent

'Riveting'

Elizabeth Day

'Acerbic brilliance . . . It is so great I am struggling to find the words to do it justice . . . Wood is an agonisingly gifted writer, so great at capturing micro-emotions, the complexity of friendship, love, mother–child tension, all done with breezy readability. At times it's funny, thought-provoking, very moving. I care so much about the characters. I am now going to read all her other books'

Marian Keyes

'A rare pleasure . . . I was shocked by how unusual it felt to spend 275 pages exclusively in the company of older women'

Sunday Times

'Glorious . . . Charlotte Wood joins the ranks of writers such as Nora Ephron, Penelope Lively and Elizabeth Strout'

Guardian

'Wood ably conveys that older women didn't used to be old, and that the experience of ageing is universally bewildering'

Lionel Shriver, *Observer*, Books of the Year

'One of those deceptively compact novels that continues to open doors in your mind long after the last page'

Patrick Gale

'A lovely, lively, intelligent, funny book'
Tessa Hadley

'Charlotte Wood's powerful novel depicts old age as a
time when hope, desire and love are still felt
as vividly as they were in youth'
Daily Mail

'These women are so alive on the page, it is impossible
not to feel a kinship and intimacy with each of them'
Daily Express

'An unflinchingly observed celebration of the profundity
and mundanity of friendship, treated with
elegance, wit, and tenderness'
Kiran Millwood Hargrave

'With the lightest of touches, this big-hearted, insightful
read tackles friendship, ambition, aging and death'
Good Housekeeping

PRAISE FOR *THE NATURAL WAY OF THINGS*

Winner, 2016 Stella Prize

Co-winner, 2016 Prime Minister's Award

Winner, Fiction Book of the Year, 2016 Indie Awards

Winner, 2016 Indie Book of the Year Award

Shortlisted, 2016 Miles Franklin Literary Award

Shortlisted, 2016 Victorian Premier's Literary Awards

Shortlisted, 2016 Barbara Jefferis Award

Shortlisted, 2016 Queensland Literary Award for Fiction

Shortlisted, 2016 Voss Literary Prize

'An unforgettable reading experience'
Liane Moriarty

'Ferorcious . . . recalls the early Elena Ferrante'
NPR

'A masterpiece'
Guardian

'Devastating'
Economist

'At once brutal and beautiful'
Kirkus

Charlotte Wood is the author of seven novels and three books of non-fiction. Her novel *The Natural Way of Things* won the 2016 Stella Prize, the Indie Book of the Year and Novel of the Year Awards, and was joint winner of the Prime Minister's Literary Award for Fiction. Her next novel, *The Weekend*, was an international bestseller and was shortlisted for the 2020 Stella Prize, the Prime Minister's Literary Award and the Australian Literature Society Gold Medal. Her features and essays have appeared in the *New York Times, Guardian, Literary Hub* and *Sydney Morning Herald*, among others. Charlotte lives in Sydney with her husband.

STONE

YARD

DEVOTIONAL

CHARLOTTE

WOOD

Sceptre

First published in Great Britain in 2023 by Sceptre
An imprint of Hodder & Stoughton
An Hachette UK company

4

A CIP catalogue record for this title is available from the British Library

Hardback ISBN 9781399724340
Trade Paperback ISBN 9781399724357
ebook ISBN 9781399724364

Printed and bound in Great Britain by Clays Ltd, Elcograf S.p.A.

Hodder & Stoughton policy is to use papers that are natural, renewable and recyclable products and made from wood grown in sustainable forests. The logging and manufacturing processes are expected to conform to the environmental regulations of the country of origin.

Hodder & Stoughton Ltd
Carmelite House
50 Victoria Embankment
London EC4Y 0DZ

www.sceptrebooks.co.uk

FOR JANE PALFREYMAN

'I felt chastened by the world.'

NICK CAVE

'This is what I have decided to do with my life just now. I will do this work of transformed and even distorted memory and lead this life, the one I am leading today.'

ELIZABETH HARDWICK

PART I

DAY ONE

ARRIVE FINALLY AT about three. The place has the feel of a 1970s health resort or eco-commune, but is not welcoming. Signs on fences, or stuck on little posts by driveways: NO ENTRY. NO PARKING. A place of industry, not recreation.

I park in a nondescript spot near a fence, and sit in the quiet car.

~

On the way here I stopped in the town and visited my parents' graves for the first time in thirty years. It took some time for me to find them in what is called the 'lawn cemetery', the newer part fenced off – why? – from the original town graveyard with its crooked rows of tilting white headstones and crosses. That old part is overlooked by enormous black pine trees; ravens and cockatoos scream from their high branches. The lawn cemetery, by contrast, is a dull, flat expanse filled with gently curved rows of low, ugly headstones of identical dimensions. Neater, I suppose (but why should a cemetery be neat?).

There is no lawn, just dusty dead grass.

To find my parents I had to recall the cold, unsheltered feeling I had – physically, I mean – at each of their funerals. There had been the sensation of too much space around me there, at the place where my father, then later my mother, were sent into their adjacent shafts of opened earth. (It seemed callous to me back then, to lower a person into a hole in the ground using ropes and cords instead of arms.) But walking around the cemetery now, remembering that sensation helped me find the spot again. I stood before my mother's and father's gravestones, two machine-cut and polished pieces of stone. The colour and design of the stones and the words on them seemed to bear no trace of either of my parents, though I must have decided on, approved of, them.

Someone had pushed some ugly plastic flowers into the small metal grate beside the headstones. Perhaps there are volunteers who go around leaving fake flowers at unvisited graves. Who else would want to mark my parents' burial place after all this time? The plastic of the flowers had turned grey, every part of them, though they must have once been luridly coloured like those I could see sticking up from the little metal vases at other headstones: ragged synthetic petals in puce and maroon and white with dark green stems, angled here and there with artificial nodules and leaves.

I stood on the grass and looked at the ugly flowers, then at my parents' names carved into each slab in front of me. And I realised: *Your bones are here, beneath my feet.* I squatted then, those few feet of earth between their bodies and mine, and I kissed my fingers and pressed them to the crackly grass.

~

Walking back to the car I remembered something else: a phone call, many months after my mother's death. A man's voice quietly telling me her headstone was ready. I recall standing by the laundry door with the phone in my hand, my outsides unaltered but everything within me plummeting. Like a sand-bank collapsing inside me.

~

Near the end of the drive the sky darkened, turned drizzly. The road coiled up a steep hill, entering a tunnel of thick bush – my car struggled on the wet bitumen – and then on the other side it opened out into these endless, shallow, angular plains, bare as rubbed suede.

Place names I thought I'd forgotten returned to me one by one: *Chakola, Royalla, Bredbo, Bunyan. Jerangle, Bobundara, Kelton Plain, Rocky Plain, Dry Plain*, like beads on a rosary. Like naming the bones of my own body.

~

A little after I arrive, the sun comes out. I get out and look around me, trying to work out where I should go. There are some skinny pencil pines, a few dripping eucalypts, a lot of silence. Three or four small wooden cabins painted a drab olive; green peaked tin roofs.

I wander the grounds for a time, eventually finding a shed marked OFFICE, and knock on the door. A woman appears, introduces herself as Sister Simone. She pronounces it *Sim*one, traces of an accent (French?). Indeterminate age, business-like but soft-looking at the same time. Scrawnyish. Quite yellow teeth. She apologises for not having come out to greet me; she is busy, but a housekeeper will show me around if I wait for a bit. She tells me with a teeth-showing smile – more a grimace – that she's looked me up on the internet and that my work sounds 'very impressive'. Her tone seems lightly insulting. I smile and tell her the internet is very misleading. She pauses, then says coolly that saving God's creatures most certainly is important work. She's slightly cross, I think. Not accustomed to disagreement. We bare our teeth at each other again and she closes the office door.

~

Anita, the housekeeper. Chatty and broad-bummed. Shivering a little in her maroon fleece vest over a turquoise shirt, navy pants. She leads me around the buildings and grounds, and I trot behind her as she rattles on. She could never be a nun – imagine getting up for Vigils at five a.m. In winter! Plus, they can't watch Netflix: 'That's never going to work for me.'

She unfolds her arms now and then to point at something – shop, old orchard, guest cabins; gestures further off to indicate the paddocks, a small dam – then refolds them against the cold and we take off towards a little stone chapel. I open my mouth to say, *It's okay, I don't need to see inside*, but don't want to be rude. We push through a big wooden door. Anita's chatter doesn't stop but turns to a whisper, though there is nobody in the church. She has just learned, she says, that this is not called a chapel – chapels are privately owned. This is a Consecrated Church. When they come in here it's called the Liturgy of the Hours, she whispers, enunciating these words as if from a foreign language. Which I suppose they are.

Anita points to a corner: 'This is where *you* sit.'

Four wooden pews off to the side, away from those in the centre of the church, which are presumably used by the sisters. The guest pews are smaller than theirs, more modern in design and made of a golden pinewood. Each place is marked with a flat, square, brown cushion, and a brown leather-padded kneeler runs the length of the pew. Anita waits for me to show her that I know how to sit. The seat is surprisingly comfortable.

There's no altar. Instead, a simple wooden lectern in front of a huge carved wooden crucifix on the whitewashed wall.

As we leave, Anita pauses to show me a large angular flower arrangement set on the floor to one side, beneath the crucifix. It was made by one of the oblates, she says. I murmur some generic sound. Yes, says Anita, sighing with admiration. This particular oblate really thinks outside the box.

I don't tell her I have no idea what an oblate is.

~

Next on my tour Anita stops at a double-doored fridge-freezer on a verandah. She yanks open the fridge door to show me the shelves containing eggs, milk, a few apples. Slams that door shut, opens the freezer to reveal individually packaged meat pies and four-slice packets of wholemeal bread. This food is for those who don't want to take lunch from the dining room, she explains.

I will not see the sisters except in church, she warns, as if I will be disappointed. The nuns live in another long low building, fenced off by a hedge behind the church, a hidden part closed to guests.

At last to my cabin, which Anita calls by a saint's name I immediately forget. The cabins nearby seem to be unoccupied, but who knows? I don't ask if there are any other guests. The place feels pretty empty.

Anita unlocks my door and stamps about opening curtains, showing me the remote control for the reverse-cycle air conditioner. ('It gets very hot here in summer, you'd be surprised, but look, it's on "heater" – see the little sunshine symbol?') She picks up a laminated booklet from the small desk – 'Everything you need to know is in here' – and slaps it down again. Waves a hand at the kitchenette with its canisters and cupboards, and then in the opposite direction to the unseen bathroom, then smiles at me and sighs with a bright finality, as if now the formalities are over we can settle down to a proper chat. I thank her briskly, stepping towards the door. She finally seems to accept that I am not looking for conversation, and leaves.

~

Alone at last, having flipped through the booklet and ferried my few things from the car, I lie on the floor in a patch of wan afternoon sunlight. The heating works well; the room is soon warm. The light from the window illuminates a small wooden crucifix positioned on the wall above the desk. The silence is so thick it makes me feel wealthy.

My phone vibrates, its buzz making me jolt. Alex has landed at Heathrow; his new colleagues are to collect him. I reply, then lie back on the floor again. Neither of us has said it yet, but we both know I won't be following. We both know he'll be relieved.

I realise that it would be possible here, once Anita had given you your key and trudged off in her sheepskin boots, to spend the entire visit without seeing or hearing another soul. It is accepted, the laminated booklet says, that guests might want total solitude, and they are free to decline joining others for eating or worship. Noise is discouraged. Nobody would have to know, until the end of one's stay, that a person might choose to end their life here on this clean carpet in a warm, silent room. At this moment I cannot think of a greater act of kindness than to offer such privacy to a stranger.

But my own escape is a different, less definitive kind than that.

From somewhere beyond my window comes the faint burbling of chickens.

~

At five o'clock I decide to try to wake myself up by joining the nuns at Vespers. I walk the track to the little church in the falling light, in the silence. My footsteps on the gravel make the only sound. I sit in the cold church and wait. I was wrong about other visitors: two women bustle to the front row of the guest pews and settle in. They seem quite at home. Then, from a door on the other side of the church, the nuns enter in ones and twos. Long brown habits, white collars. Some of them tuck their hands into the apron fronts of their gowns. One very old woman arrives in an electric wheelchair, jerking slightly to cross the lip of the entrance way. Another uses a walking frame. There are eight altogether, at least half of them quite elderly. Sister Simone is there. She doesn't look in the direction of our seats; none of them does.

Their pews have panelled wooden fronts, so they are visible only from the waist up. They begin to sing a series of prayers I find it impossible to locate in either of the two photocopied booklets on my seat, one with a musical score and another with the words of the psalms. The nuns have very high, thin voices, some quite lovely. It's a kind of chanting, the same seven or eight notes released, over and over. There is another congregant a few pews behind me. A man's quiet, low voice, a throat clearing softly now and then. The singing is mesmerising, until I find the right page in the right booklet and discover that the lyrics are all about denouncing evil this and God's enemies that. The subtlety of the lilting chant belies the blunt instrument of the words themselves.

Watching the women, I'm convinced that the words they're singing are meaningless; that instead, this ritual is all about the body and the unconscious mind. Every so often, at some signal I can't discern, they bow very deeply in their little wooden pews, so they disappear for a minute. Then they pop up again. I keep thinking of yoga: it has the same rhythmic quiet, the same slow, feminine submission.

At the end, I sit for a moment after the nuns and then the women in front of me (and the unseen man) have filed out. By the time I leave the church, it is completely empty. I walk back to my cabin in the dusk.

It's shockingly peaceful.

I eat two bowls of peanuts and drink three glasses of wine for dinner.

My back is very painful now, worsened by the six hours of driving and the hard wooden pew, despite its cushion. I lie on the carpet, arms outstretched. When I wake I see Jesus on his cross, looking down at me.

DAY TWO

SLEPT POORLY. THE light from the green exit sign above my cabin door was too bright, and the ticking and cracking of the wooden building in the wind kept me awake. I get up at five thirty and shower, then make coffee. Manage to hotspot to my phone momentarily – reception very poor, but that is supposed to be the point of coming here – and download a short cheerful email from Alex, and a few others. Read some of them but can't face answering any. I should have set up an auto-reply, but even that seemed an impossible task. I sit with my coffee at the little wooden desk and watch the sky slowly lightening beyond the spires of the pencil pines. I listen to the wind as it gradually drops.

At seven thirty I go, out of curiosity, to Lauds. (What else did I imagine I'd be doing here? Sleeping, I think. Deciding, perhaps, about Alex, my work. Crying. Hiding.) As I close my cabin door in the sunrise, the cold clean air moving down from the mountains, and the taste of that air, comes to me as if from childhood.

The sun is lifting and it streams into the church each time the big wooden door opens. The nuns enter quietly. The one with the walking frame arrives first. She might play the organ, though from my seat near the back of the guest pews I can't see around the corner. Another lights the candles – one near their door, another by the lectern and two on the floor, at the foot of the big crucifix.

The singing is transporting, especially when they harmonise. One nun leads a psalm and the others do a repeated chorus. Lauds, like Vespers, goes for half an hour.

After this comes the Eucharist (which might also be called Terce?) at nine o'clock.

During Lauds I found I was thinking, *But how do they get anything done?* All these interruptions day in, day out, having to drop what you're doing and toddle into church every couple of hours. Then I realised: it's not an interruption to the work; it is the work. This *is* the doing.

~

The candles in the church are plain and white with a pleasant smell. Sort of herbal or cinnamony. A hint of incense, but not overpowering.

In the church, a great restfulness comes over me. I try to think critically about what's happening but I'm drenched in a weird tranquillity so deep it puts a stop to thought. Is it to do with being almost completely passive, yet still somehow participant? Or perhaps it's simply owed to being somewhere so *quiet*; a place entirely dedicated to silence. In the contemporary world, this kind of stillness feels radical. Illicit.

~

Later in the day I turn up again, at Middle Hour. It's only about twenty minutes long. The same little tune is used for the various psalms, the same fatigue overwhelms me, and I can barely stay awake. Their singing is a chiming, medieval sort of sound: unexpected and unbalanced, yet melodious, in those thin reedy voices. They sing everything very slowly. It's hypnotic. The words seem to make no sense. There's a lot about evil-doers trying to destroy the psalm's narrator. *All day long they crush me.* Foes and enemies, intent on massacre and annihilation. All this warbled by a bunch of nuns way out here on the high, dry Monaro plains, far from anywhere.

At the end of the Middle Hour, two approach the centre from opposite sides of the church, bow to the crucifix, then turn and bow to each other, then they leave. The next two arrive at the centre, bow to Jesus and then to each other. And so on, until there is nobody left.

~

Lunch is either to be 'shared at table with other guests' – no thank you – or a takeaway affair. I set off with my basket and a couple of containers from my cabin, down to the dining room. When Anita described this arrangement it sounded romantic, taking your basket and filling it with food. Images of wicker and chequered tea towels, Red Riding Hood-style. But it turns out the basket is the gaudy plastic kind used in the supermarket express lane. The decor (if that is what you can call it in a nunnery) is very simple, sort of innocent and somehow poignant. Like the house of an elderly aunt, but with crucifixes instead of 'Bless this house' plaques. Today's lunch is thick slices of cooked ham, some bright yellow chutney, a plain green salad with a bottle of 'Italian dressing' nearby, and roast carrots, potatoes and parsnip, all a little hard. Plus a big vat of sticky-looking mashed potato that I avoid. The dessert is some kind of apple pudding. The pudding is good; everything else is ordinary. You wouldn't want to eat this stuff every day of your life. The other guests – the two women, anyway; I haven't seen the man – don't look up when we pass each other. Which is fine by me.

Lunch is the main meal of the day, and we are to assemble our own dinners from one of the many packets or single-serve tins in one's room. I'm saving two slices of lunch ham to have for supper with baked beans. The cupboards in my room are like some kind of storeroom from one of the country motels of my childhood. Everything's packaged in individual sachets and servings – Nescafé, sugar, Vegemite, margarine, teabags. Teensy cans of Heinz spaghetti or baked beans, or tuna. Little boxes of highly processed breakfast cereal. There are biscuits in two-packs; Scotch Fingers, Jatz. And tiny individual packets of cheese slices in the bar fridge. Something makes me wonder if all this has been donated by some corporation or other. When I first saw all that packaging I couldn't stop my tears coming, which was ridiculous. But something about the nasty little packets overcame me; it was to do with splitting everything into awful, unnatural fragments. The loneliness and waste of it. And a polluted feeling: even here, the inescapable imperative to generate garbage. Surely, if God exists, He could not approve of all this *rubbish*. Yet I have brought with me, quite against the spirit of the place, my own rubbish – blocks of chocolate, packages of salted peanuts, blueberries in a plastic carton, coffee, wine. He probably wouldn't approve of that either.

17

Being here feels somehow like childhood; the hours are so long and there is so much waiting, staring into space. Absolutely nothing is asked of me, nothing expected.

~

I think of wandering to the shop to buy some candles. If there are any plain ones like those in the church, I would like to take one home. But instead of taking that three-minute walk I lie on the floor again and fall into a syrupy sleep.

Later, around four, I do visit the shop. There is nothing of interest to buy. Many hideous greeting cards, some of which bear religious images, but mostly they are just bad paintings of flowers. The Handmade Candles are especially ugly, garishly coloured and decorated with lumpy gold scrolls and astrological-looking designs. I do buy a plain sandalwood-scented candle, a plastic torch and a wooden cross. The cross has rounded edges and fits snugly in the hand. I am a bit ashamed of it. I don't know why I buy it, except maybe as a mark of respect to these people, and as a kind of talisman, to hold and feel. It is for the body, not the mind.

~

Vespers again. There is one spoken element that disrupts the singing; 'prayers of the faithful' is the phrase that bubbles up from my childhood. 'We pray for a marriage that is breaking down,' one of the sisters says. I look at the floor. I think about Alex, but he's free. He needs no prayers from me.

Then this: 'We pray for all those who will die tonight.'

~

After my parents died – not together, though close enough in time to fuse inside my primitive self, inside my dreams and my body, into a single catastrophe – for many years I felt as though I were breathing and moving through some kind of glue. I could not have said this then. If someone had asked me how I felt, I would not have been able to answer. The only true reply would have been: *I don't know.*

The day after I learned that my mother's illness would not be cured I kept a doctor's appointment in the inner city, where I lived then. When I entered the room and the doctor asked brightly how I was, I began to cry, and then – embarrassed – explained. She asked about my father, and when I told her he was dead she asked about the kind of counselling my mother and I had sought when he died. I was mystified. As far as I knew there was no such thing as counselling in our town.

She then told me I was clever, and right, to seek help now. But I only came here for a pap test, I said through my tears. She handed me a tissue box and said we would do the test another time. She asked me about my parents, and listened for some time. Towards the end of the consultation she recommended I see a bereavement counsellor. She herself was not a trained counsellor, only a general practitioner, and a specialist would be better able to help me. She wrote the name and address of the centre on a piece of paper.

Can't I just talk to you? I asked her.

And so I did. I went to see her three times.

The doctor was big and square and imperious. For some reason her authority and her deep, practical kindness made me assume she was gay. She did not gush or emote, which was a relief. If someone had been openly empathetic, if I'd been entreated to elaborate upon the emotional terrain of what was now being called my grief, I would have been ashamed.

On my second visit, I remarked (embarrassed again by my tears) that it seemed my friends were deserting me, just when I needed them most. She was unsurprised. Your life has been stripped down to bedrock, she said. It's not their fault; their lives are protected by many layers of cushioning, and they can't understand or acknowledge this difference between you. It probably frightens them. They're not trying to hurt you.

She didn't say, *Understand this: you are alone*, but that is what I heard. I found it strangely comforting. She said again, I think you should call the bereavement centre.

The last time I saw the doctor, she seemed weary of me and my problems. She asked from behind her desk, a little testily: What is it that you want right now?

For this not to be happening, I said. I could hear the sullenness in my voice.

The doctor looked at me and waited for a moment. She seemed to decide on the simple, brutal truth. Well, it's happening, she said.

I have always been grateful to her.

DAY THREE

SLEPT DEEP AND long this time. I covered the exit sign with my jacket last night so it was much darker, and without any wind the night was quiet.

In Lauds again, I wonder if they think boredom is a sin. Do all religions include some form of this repetitive movement? It feels ancient, superstitious. Walking in circles, bowing and prostrating, kneeling and standing. What is its purpose? Eradication of the ego, in some way? Denying the human craving for newness, or escape, or surprise? Returning and returning and returning, a prescribed revisiting. Watching them do their thing, I wonder if the nuns annoy each other. Whether one's very low bowing is seen as pretentious by another; or if another's failure to hit the right note drives her neighbour nuts. It seems impossible that this sort of emotional life would not be carrying on beneath the silence. Today's psalms were not so full of evil foes but there was a lot of nationhood-praise stuff. The Lord has made our borders safe and filled our fields with harvest etc. Much celebration of all the good things He has brought to our land . . . I struggle to see the relevance of any of it to these women and their lives. What is the meaning of this ancient Hebrew bombast about enemies and borders and persecution? What's the point of their singing about it day after day after day?

~

At ten, I'm reading in my room when a *leaf blower* starts up outside! I leap to my window to see one of the stouter nuns wielding the hateful thing, revving it, trudging along the pathway, turning slowly from side to side, pointlessly scattering leaves. It goes for about two minutes.

~

I'm becoming a little afraid the tranquillised feeling will never lift. I could just leave, but the effort of even packing my bag feels beyond me. Instead, at noon I go to something called the Lectio Divina with a Sister Bonaventure. When I arrive I'm pretty sure she is the leaf blower nun, but I don't say anything.

23

The Lectio Divina, she explains in a low, husky voice, is 'divine reading'; a slow, contemplative reading of a bit of gospel (which she hands out printed on pieces of paper). The other people in the room are the two women, who are called Diane and Cynthia and have come from Melbourne; another woman I have not seen before, called Lavinia; and a man called Richard, who seems to live locally. I think it may have been his voice I heard in the church behind me that first day, and there is something distantly familiar about him.

We sit on plastic chairs in a circle and go around the room, each person reading a paragraph aloud. After each reading there is silence for several minutes, during which you are to think about what you have heard. Then you are supposed to say aloud any word that has struck you or troubled you or caught your attention. After this the reading begins again, with the next paragraph. The same process of thinking and offered words or phrases follows, but during a longer period of silence. When that is done, Sister Bonaventure reads the whole piece again. More silence, then a discussion. She says the piece today has suddenly revealed itself to her as about obedience – which is handy, because there's a novice she's looking after who's just up to the obedience part of her vows. People throw in words here and there. Richard is the only one closely attending as he reads, considering for potential meaning – the others go through the motions, offering banal observations in an effort to score brownie points from Sister Bonaventure. Cynthia from Melbourne (whom Bonaventure calls 'Wendy'; a patient glance between Cynthia and Diane makes me think this has been going on for days) is especially obsequious, marvelling over every word of the paragraph. Bonaventure seems to be just tolerating her. My own thoughts are not interesting, except as arguments against what the Scriptures are saying. Which I don't think is the purpose of the exercise, so I keep my mouth shut.

Despite this, the process is strangely beautiful. Sister Bonaventure says getting caught on a word is the point, and that if you remain troubled or confused by it, you just 'hand it over to God'. This is so antithetical to everything I have believed (knowledge is power, question everything, take responsibility) that it feels almost wicked. The astonishing – suspect – simplicity of just . . . handing it over.

(Later in the day, from somewhere in my memory comes an artist I once saw on television, peering at a canvas as he worked. He quoted Kipling: 'When your Daemon is in charge, do not try to think consciously. Drift, wait, and obey.')

Sister Bonaventure says in passing that when she entered the 'monastery' – she keeps using the word *monastic* rather than any nun-specific terminology – she was worried about growing bored. But then she laughs, as if the notion is ludicrous. 'Never a dull moment,' she says. I can tell she means it.

~

Afterwards, as I'm pushing open the door to my cabin, it comes to me: the man is Richard *Gittens*, from high school! A wash of fondness comes at the memory of his fuzzy, light-reddish hair and skinny body, his amused, modest way of being. The body is thicker, the hair shorn close now, grey and mostly gone, but the self-irony, it seems, remains.

~

Lunch is tepid ricotta lasagne and a watery cauliflower, carrot and broccoli 'cheese'. A reasonable kind of tabouli – made with pearl barley, I think. Everything is severely under-seasoned (though at least yesterday's ham was salty). Very glad I brought the peanuts, which I keep scoffing for the salt. There is a creamy-looking cake I skip, but I flip into my basket several tins of peaches to eat for breakfast with yoghurt, as I've eaten all my berries.

~

'Action is the antidote to despair.' Joan Baez.
   'First, do no harm.' Hippocrates.

It occurs to me yet again that not only have I – I, we, the centre – comprehensively failed in our one objective (the hollow joke we used to make about it: Threatened Species Rescue Centre, clue's in the name . . .), but at every step of my every attempt I have only worsened the destruction. Every email, meeting, press release, conference, protest. Every minuscule action after waking means slurping up resources, expelling waste, destroying habitat, causing ruptures of some other kind. Whereas staying still, suspended in time like these women, does the opposite. They are *doing no harm*.

On the other hand, 'Evil flourishes . . .'

(Also – what about all that packaging?)

~

I'm growing accustomed to the bell now, that rings for the nuns at each of the liturgical hours. It's not meant for us civilians, but I hear its faint sound coming from the sisters' quarters beyond the church, and find myself listening for it.

On the walk back from Vespers I look up and see the cold white moon rising behind the black trees.

DAY FOUR

I WAKE AT five fifteen and stay in bed until six, while the room warms up. It is much colder this morning, drizzling outside. I feel surprisingly light compared to the past few days, as if I have regained a great deal of energy. As if finally emerging from a deeply necessary period of sedation.

The mid-morning service is the same, ish. But at a certain point, one of the nuns – I like the look of her, tall and narrow with a big rosy nose and steely grey hair visible at the edges of her veil – steps across the church and asks me to move to the other side of the crucifix. I stand there with Cynthia from Melbourne and then the others – Diane and Lavinia, plus another two men and a woman I've not seen before – and the nuns gather into a large, closed circle. (No sign of Richard

Gittens today. If it is even him. I wonder whether, if I told him my name, any recognition at all would cross his face?)

I suddenly realise, too late to return to my seat, that I'm about to take part in communion. When the old nun says, 'The body of Christ,' and puts the wafer into my hand I have forgotten what to say, but it swims up from distant childhood: 'Amen.' The wafer is chalky white, the size of a twenty-cent piece, with an indented cross pressed into it. When I put it in my mouth it dissolves immediately. Utterly tasteless, like paper. It seems thinner or finer than the ones from childhood, which I recall as hard, slightly wheaty-tasting discs sticking to the roof of your mouth. I feel silly taking it now, of course. I can't recall the last time I took communion. My mother's funeral? I'm not sure I would even have done it then; I'd abandoned all this long before that.

Afterwards comes the sign of peace. The nuns move towards us with their hands outstretched – and something catches in me. I allow myself to be greeted in turn by three or four of them; a very young woman with a clear, open face, wearing a synthetic black puffy vest over her habit (I feel sure she is the novice Bonaventure was talking about), and a few of the others. I find it hard to stop tears pricking my eyes, which alarms me. It is to do with being greeted warmly by a stranger, offered peace for no reason, without question. They have kind faces; warmth radiates from them. I hold their soft, dry hands.

After this it's back to our seats for more praying and singing, more biblical mumbo jumbo. I drift off and think about my feet being cold, and my legs. Listen to the woman behind me – Lavinia? – singing very badly off-key.

Nothing now till Vespers at five. It's still drizzling, and grows even colder as I walk back to my cabin. I crank up the heating.

~

When I was about six or seven my mother used to visit a blind woman called Denise, who lived in a caravan with a series of annexes on a property outside town. She had a small feeble child, frighteningly pale-skinned, and a huge bearded husband. When my mother arrived with me in tow, the husband gruffly and immediately left the caravan to go across the yard into one of his sheds, or climbed into his truck and drove away. The yard was filled with old cars and rusted machinery, and steel drums, inert, on the dirt.

I don't know how my mother befriended Denise, who had thick black hair cut in a blunt style and spoke out into the room in a dry, even voice. I felt it was wrong for me to be there in her home, watching the sickly baby crawling about. I didn't like looking at Denise, and I never spoke, but she and my mother would talk easily together for what felt like hours. Sometimes Denise would get up and make a cup of tea, or peel some carrots for her family's dinner, speaking upwards into the air before her, her eyelids flickering softly. I didn't like the sense that I was spying on Denise, but that was how I felt.

There seemed something sinister about the little caravan parked in the dirt with the rocks and rusted things strewn about it, and it was sad to me that Denise could not see the bleakness of her home. At the same time, I knew she was alert to my mute presence, and I think now my child self feared that in her blindness she discerned things about me that I, and even my mother, did not know.

Denise never repaid my mother's visits. There was, in her home, an air of captivity. When her husband returned to the caravan, we would leave.

Once I heard someone – a neighbour – tell my mother it was good of her to visit Denise. It had never occurred to me that my mother was there to look after Denise, to 'mind' her, as people said about children. I just thought they were friends.

When I was older, a boyfriend of mine said with a kind of a sneer, 'What *was* your mother, some kind of missionary?'

No, I said. She was just kind.

It's possible, of course, that I am wrong about this. It's possible Denise and her husband didn't welcome my mother's arrival at all; perhaps they endured her visits with me – the mute, anxious child – out of politeness or some other pragmatic necessity. But still, it has surprised me, over the years, to discover how many people find the idea of habitual kindness to be somehow suspect: a mask or a lie. My mother did have an uncommon sort of simplicity, a light oddity, about her. But I still believe the answer I gave my boyfriend was the truth.

~

Just now I went down alone to the empty church and sat for a time.

Back in my room, it's odd to find myself longing for Vespers. I suppose it might be like this in prison. You look forward to the routines because they show that time has passed. And now the tranquillised feeling has lifted I'm too alert, reading for a while but not falling asleep. I keep checking my emails, longing for distraction, but still can't bring myself to answer any.

~

I go to Vespers expecting more of the same, and by now am at ease sitting at the front of the guest pews. I'm surprised to see several of the nuns already in situ, ten minutes before start time, and then the organist starts playing quite loudly and comparatively jauntily. It's as if everybody has been suddenly energised by some unseen force. Busy things take place: scurrying about with gold staffs and a crucifix on a stick; lighting of incense and lots of candles, putting them in position in their holders, taking them out and fitting them back in. Then suddenly, in place of the usual soundless and modest entry in pairs and threes, there is a *procession*: one nun leading with the crucifix on the pole, followed by two more, their tall white candles held before them, then the young novice carrying incense, strong clouds of it billowing, and then the rest of the women entering two by two. It is stark and mighty and beautiful to see them all lined up, with the incense rising, the candles and the music. Each pair comes to the centre, bows in unison, and then each woman bows to her partner, separates and moves to her pew – a mirror image of the other day's departure.

The singing is unearthly this evening.

At one point the two soloists who have been singing each day – Sister Bonaventure, who has a strong, clear voice, and the young novice – move to the back of the church to stand in front of the organ and sing a two-part harmony. The novice walks like a bashful teenage boy. I have watched her each time in church; she stands with her feet apart, firmly planted, shoulders a bit hunched, hands in her puffy vest pockets or, if she's not wearing it, tucked into the front of her tunic. Her voice – delicate, reaching, yearning – is the opposite of her physical bearing. The two of them muck it up here and there; I can tell from the way they smile at each other as they sing. But the sound soars.

Sister Simone is there, sprinkling holy water over us guests at the start, and again at the end. We are directed to gather in the centre of the church and give praise to a Madonna-and-child image – the nuns sing in Latin, and we outsiders awkwardly nod along. Then we line up in pairs for the final sprinkling. I am next to the old nun in the electric wheelchair. She smiles at me with what feels like her whole self, and I can only think of it as . . . love.

Afterwards I walk back to the cabin and lie on the floor again for a long time.

~

Bedrock was the word my doctor had used.

Driving across the surface of the high stony plains on my way here, I found the landscape's desolation beautiful. My car had been seized now and then by the wind, and I had to grip the steering wheel to correct its movement along the empty road. The sweeping, broad structure of this land gently shifts from one plane into another, each sloping yet almost flat, like a shoulder blade. Although these plains bristle with a fine skin of pale grasses, they are almost as bare as bedrock, and I wonder if this is why I never came back, until now.

~

I've started packing. I'll load the car first thing in the morning, then take a quick walk to try to loosen my spine before the long drive home. With a few stops I should be back by around five. Maybe grab dinner at the sushi place.

DAY FIVE

BEFORE GETTING IN the car I walk up a path into a patch of
bush and see a lyrebird poking and digging at the side of the
track. I stand for ages and watch it. It seems completely unperturbed by my presence.

PART II

A HEAVY SPRING frost this morning. Crossing the grass I made a clean track of footprints, deep green on the white spread of the lawn. It returned me to my childhood, to the sense of secret authority, imprinting one's presence into a place with those clear, sharp prints. *I exist.* The private, pleasurable sound of the finest layer of ice breaking beneath the weight of each step.

~

We've had to give up Anita, the housekeeper. There's not enough money. It always seemed silly to me anyway, not to clean the guest rooms ourselves along with our own. But some are not happy about it, even though we have no guests now. Anita herself appears completely untroubled, which is a relief. We had a small morning tea to farewell her, and gathered around as Simone gave her the gift of a St Anthony medal, and a card on which we had each written a personal message of gratitude and our wishes for her future. Anita opened the box first and said, 'Oh, wow,' in an uninterested way, and then shoved the card in its envelope and the medal with it into her bag. She has a new job at the day spa in the fancy hotel in town and seems delighted, despite the fact they are paying her even less than we did.

It's more than four years since I met her on that first visit here, and still I know almost nothing of her life. Is this good or bad? Probably neither. I don't think she minds. I don't think she has much curiosity about the way we live. I doubt she noticed the day or even the year I drove into the sisters' car park instead of the guests'.

I think to Anita we remain a foreign species. And why not? We've done it deliberately; made ourselves foreign to ordinary life.

~

White things, in this (my) room: Old wall radiator coated in thick creamy paint. Square porcelain basin, bulbous chrome taps (hard to turn on cold mornings – poorly designed with nothing to grip). White melamine bathroom cabinet above the basin, mirror on the inside door so as not to encourage vanity. Electrical outlet, power cord. Canvas roller blind with grimy tassel. Spoked plastic laundry hanger with pegs for drying underwear, right now hooked from the overhead brass light fitting. Cardboard tissue box, printed for some reason with pictures of teddy bears. Strip of paracetamol tablets on the basin edge. Wooden bedside lamp, paint peeling slightly at the base. Large coffee mug printed with a black ink portrait and signature of Thomas Hardy, whose books I have never read. I don't remember where it came from, but, inexplicably, I brought it here with me. Small fluted ceramic vase (empty) on windowsill. Cotton waffle-weave blanket, bringing comfort when the bed is made and sharply tucked, evoking the brisk practical kindness of mothers or nurses.

Lists like this show how much one really does have, on those days one falls into thinking of life – bedroom, relationships, intellectual life, spirit – as empty.

~

The last time I drove here – when I came 'for good', you might say, though I didn't know that was what it would turn out to be – I stopped at my parents' graves once more. I had not felt the need to go there every time, but on that day I crouched beside my mother's headstone again and tugged at the desiccating plastic sticks of those same ugly fake flowers, which were surprisingly difficult to wrench from the grip of the little grate.

Every grave had one of these metal cups set into its headstone for filling with water to keep real flowers alive, but none had any living flowers that I could see. I found the plastic more than usually offensive, given my mother's occupation (florist). She never used the word 'common', but throughout my childhood I knew that this was what plastic flowers were. Once I removed them, I placed on top of the metal grate a small white ridged ceramic pot I had brought with me for this purpose. It was planted with two little grey-blue trailing succulents. It would be nice if the plants, chosen for their hardiness, could multiply and grow out of the pot, and somehow creep over the headstone. But it wouldn't be like that. If they escaped from the pot and took hold in the earth, the council would mow over the top of them. But probably they would die first, for lack of rain or too much, or they would be knocked over by a prowling cat, or the pot emptied and taken by someone who wanted it.

I chucked the plastic stems and fake petal rags into the big green wheelie bin by the cemetery gates, and I left there and drove here, past the names on signposts, those words – Cooba, Myack, Coolringdon, Myalla, Maffra – returning to my body again.

~

I think mice have been into the poultry feed. And this morning I found one of the baby chicks dead, killed by the frost. Somehow it had strayed, was not hiding underneath its mother with the others. I picked it up, icy cold and light as a ping-pong ball, and carried it away from the chookyard in my pocket. I dug a small hole behind the compost bays for its burial. When I pushed the shovel blade into the hard ground, what came to me were the mass graves in which nuns (Irish, American, Canadian, why not also Australian?) had buried babies they called *illegitimate*. I had a terrible picture of it – a long white habit flapping, a black boot on a shovel, a hole. When I'd dug my own hole I reached into my pocket and crouched down to let the fluffy little body roll into it. Filled it back in, pressed the earth down. Said a small blessing to the chick. Not a prayer; something I made up. Maybe it was a prayer.

I could have put the little chick into the compost but it seemed disrespectful. And there are mice in there too; I can hear them moving every time I go to empty the compost bucket. Ordinarily I'd be fearing summer's arrival of the snakes, yet today find myself willing them to come. The sound of the mice makes me shudder. It's the hiddenness, I think. And that the noise stops when I get near: they're sensing me more acutely than I sense them.

When I tamped down the little chicken's grave with my own black boot, I thought of those babies and those poor girls, and the savagery of the Catholic Church came flooding in once again.

Yet here I am. Wrestle, wrestle.

WHEN YOU'RE INSIDE a church, I have come to realise, it's impossible to see out. There are no clear windows. Light streams in through the stained glass, making coloured lozenges on the floor. More light than you'd imagine is possible comes through those tall narrow slits of crisscrossed glass – but everything outside is invisible, save a rippled blur seen through the watery colourless diamonds interspersed with yellow or red or indigo. The only way to see the world beyond the church is through the door: in or out. I mentioned this yesterday to Simone as we were drying dishes. She looked at me with pity. That's a rather clumsy metaphor, she said. What I had meant was that it is peaceful there, between four thick stone walls, allowing yourself to rest in the coloured light. But I didn't say anything like that to Simone, who had turned away and, anyway, why did I care what she thought? The beauty of being here is largely the silence, after all. Not having to explain, or endlessly converse.

~

More concern, this afternoon, about money. It was a surprise when I first arrived: nothing comes from the Church. Whatever Rome does with its millions, it seems not a cent comes here. We have meetings about money: how to get it, how not to spend it. How not to waste anything. Before we had to close the guesthouse it was all about what to sell in the shop, which items sold well – the plainer candles and the honey, but not so much Sissy's beautiful cards, who could say why? (I could have said why.) Very early on I brought up the food business – all that packaged rubbish. They should buy in bulk, make things from whole ingredients. Simone looked at me in eager relief and said, 'Oh, *good*. Do you want to take over with that?' And so I began to cook, grow a few vegetables, an eternal competition with the possums and rabbits, and run the chickens. Most of my meals in the beginning – things like dhal, or vegetable tagines – were not popular with the sisters. I was told I would need to tread carefully. When I asked what they most liked to eat back then, Carmel – who had been mainly responsible for the food – walked me into the pantry. 'We like to eat the food we eat now,' she said, smiling with resentment, arms crossed, nursing the big square

45

box of her bust. In the pantry were jars and bottles and boxes: Creamy Carbonara, Tuna Bake, Three Cheeses Mac N Cheese. Later, passing through the kitchen when I was chopping eggplant or soaking chickpeas, she'd say, 'Ooh, that looks healthy.' Recruiting anyone else in the vicinity: 'Josephine, look, doesn't that look healthy?' I cut down on the spices and made sure there was potato a couple of times a week, and a truce was slowly reached. Last week she even said she 'loved' the Malaysian curry! (It had potato.)

This afternoon the talk was about whether to agist some more livestock to earn a little money. If we have to do it, please can it be sheep, not cattle like that other time? I pleaded. The sound of the mothers separated from their calves had been intolerable. All night and day they moaned and cried, the babies on one side of the fence and the mothers on the other. I would lie in bed, looking up at the arched window, and pray for the truck to arrive and take them all away. I was aware that this prayer was only for my benefit. There was no use praying for the cows and the calves. They were already dead.

Absolutely not, I couldn't stand it. I said that, about cattle, this afternoon. Simone raised an eyebrow at me. Afterwards she told me that she'd taken one look at me back on that first day and knew it would be obedience that would make or break things for me here.

Didn't need to add that the jury is still out.

~

Once, when I was in high school, a boy's mother was killed on the highway on a rainy night. She was moving cattle off the road. She had rounded a corner in her car and come upon two bullocks in the middle of the road, only just braking in time to avoid colliding with the animals. She put on her hazard lights and got out to chase the cattle off the road, up onto the verge, to stop this happening to anyone else. But a car did come, slipping fast along the wet road from the other direction, and in the dark the driver didn't see her until too late. When the boy came back to school – only a few days later – it was difficult to look at him, though we did, from a distance. He moved and spoke as usual, but there was something important about him now, and we did not know how we should behave. My friends and I lay on the oval and watched him talking with his friends, and he had a special dignity and power, hidden from us, but which we knew was in him now. To my knowledge, nobody made any mention of his mother, then or later. I was awed by him; by his appearance at school, by his sitting in his usual seat, carrying his usual schoolbag. There was something, I realised later, that I thought almost holy about the solemn, secret life he was now compelled to live outside of school, away from us. He played cricket all summer, his long legs and strong arms propelling him smoothly about the field in his whites. He was a good cricketer.

There were other motherless, fatherless children at our school, of course. But unlike the boy whose mother died in the accident, they had always been that way, and I didn't think to imagine their grief. I secretly watched them too, though more coldly. Lacking the accident's transforming cinematic tragedy, there seemed something morally distasteful – something dirty or poverty-stricken – in the way these other children lived in this broken way, seemingly without shame. I could not have known that within months of my leaving school my own father would die, and it would be my turn to move from one state to the other, from watcher to watched.

A WOMAN IN a magazine speaks of the diary she wrote as a child, in a concentration camp. 'What is most striking to me today about the diary I kept seventy-five years ago is what I left out.'

Nobody will read this but me. Even so, I imagine there are things I'm leaving out.

SIMONE CAME TO us in the vegetable garden. 'I have to tell you something,' she said, and I stood holding my rake with its steel claws pressed into the ground, my chin resting on the handle's glossy wooden tip. That rake has been here for a long time. How many sisters have held it? I thought Simone was coming to tell us about the mulch, which is due – Richard Gittens is to collect it from a nursery over the hill that sometimes donates materials to us.

But Simone was not talking about the mulch. 'Sit down, Bonaventure,' she said, which I took to refer to the fact of Bonaventure's angina issues in the past, and then I thought it was a death she was coming to deliver to us.

Bonaventure thought so too, because her mouth opened in fear and she sat down suddenly on the treated pine edging of the raised bed, leaning forward to keep her balance, her big sturdy feet on the ground.

It was not a death. Simone said, 'This is very . . .' and then closed her mouth. She looked at Bonaventure in fright, and then some understanding flowed between them which did not include me. They have known each other for half their lives.

'They've found her,' Simone said.

For one stilled moment Bonaventure stared – and Simone shook her head sharply, twice – and from Bonaventure then there came a huge inhalation, and sobbing. It was a deep release of some old and private pain. Simone, too, was crying now. She put her thin arms around her friend hunched there on the ledge, big face pushed into her hands, moaning.

I stood with my rake and could do nothing but watch the two women, hear this long-buried and dreadful grief erupting from the heart, the gut.

I stood in witness. It was all I could do.

Eventually Simone, wiping her eyes and then pushing a balled-up handkerchief into the other woman's hand, straightened and pulled Bonaventure up with her, and the two of them trudged across the grass, climbed into the truck. They did not look back at me as they drove off up the track.

I shovelled the compost and spread it, shovelled and spread, preparing the soil and waiting for things to make sense. Tried to attend, very softly and quietly, which is the closest I can get to prayer.

~

Composting was one of the things my mother did that other mothers did not. In our town, when I was a child, deliberately leaving vegetables and bones to rot in your own backyard was not something that nice people did. Some of my friends' farms had their own rubbish tips in a corner of their property, where bags of household rubbish would be thrown along with broken chairs or plates or transistor radios or machinery parts, but that was not the same. My mother's composting, right there in our yard, seemed at that time something primitive and dirty, the sort of thing an animal would do – hoarding old food and burying it! She would collect our food scraps in stray plastic containers – a margarine or an ice-cream tub – and throw the contents into the mucky bank of dirt and eggshells and rhubarb leaves at the back of the garden. Then she would bring the stained plastic containers back and wash them, ready to use again. Sometimes the compost pile smelled sour but mostly it was a dank, mouldy kind of smell. Things slithered in the pile: worms, and clouds of small flies, and unseen scuttling creatures. I don't remember there ever being snakes, but there may have been. When my schoolfriends came to our house to play I was embarrassed by the dirty plastic containers waiting on our kitchen benchtop, and hoped they wouldn't be seen.

~

After supper tonight Simone and Bonaventure sat us down and told us this.

Jennifer Tully, Sister Jenny, joined the community here and professed her solemn vows in 1983, the same year as Bonaventure. But Jenny left six years later because, she said, God had called her to work with the poor. Against advice, she moved to Bangkok with another nun, Andrea Barry, to set up a shelter for abused women. They were not welcome; they were accused of imposing their Western ethos on an Asian culture, and it was a dangerous enterprise. Their work was discouraged by the Church and by everyone else, except a few fearless Thai women. But they stayed, and their shelter for 'battered women' was always full.

In February 1998 Sister Andrea was forced to return to Australia for breast cancer treatment, but Sister Jenny stayed behind in Bangkok. One day an American Catholic priest called David Strang came to the shelter gates. Jenny had taken in a local woman who had worked as Strang's housekeeper; she had run away from his presbytery, claiming he'd repeatedly assaulted her. Sister Jenny told the women in the shelter to lock themselves inside the building, and went to speak to Father David on the street, securing the gates behind her. When she refused to open the gates or the house, Strang began shouting at her, and then he gripped her by the wrists. He dragged Jenny away, according to the women who had watched from an upper-storey window. Sister Jenny was never seen again. Days later, Strang was found hanged in the presbytery. There was no proper police investigation of Sister Jenny's disappearance and no inquest. The Church let the matter quickly fade from notice. Jenny was forty-one when she vanished.

Bonaventure and Simone sat in the worn blue velvet armchairs in our living room telling us all this. She was my beloved friend, Bonaventure said. The two women spoke for some time, smiling when they remembered starting out in this life with Jenny, tearful when they came to the part about her disappearance. At first they did not give up hope, they told us. There were a few fleeting stories in the Australian news media. They prayed and prayed, and the local people searched and searched for Sister Jenny, but she was never found.

Once it was accepted that she was surely dead and that David Strang had murdered her, there was talk of sainthood for the way she had protected the women in her care. This was encouraged by Jenny's older brother and sister, who wanted Jenny nominated as Australia's second saint. But the case never proceeded beyond some preliminary submissions to the Vatican. Some of the locals called Jenny a saint anyway, and made a memorial to her in the grounds of the women's shelter. Jenny's brother died eight years ago, and her sister, Elaine, was now in a nursing home, very frail, with Alzheimer's disease. In the wider world Sister Jenny had been forgotten, Simone said. Until now.

Heavy rains in Bangkok in the past year, she told us, caused flooding in the area near where David Strang had lived and worked. A large tree in the old presbytery grounds fell because its roots could no longer support it. The tree began to float in the floodwaters, and then someone saw, caught in the roots of the floating tree, a long bone which looked like a human tibia, and then part of a rib cage. In the following months almost all the bones belonging to Sister Jenny were recovered and identified – first, from a gold cross on a chain, then shoes and clothing and, finally, DNA. And now Jenny was coming home – 'to us,' whispered Bonaventure, weeping into a ball of tissues.

What she meant, it slowly became clear, was that the bones of Sister Jenny were to be delivered here, to the abbey, to be buried. We didn't quite understand at first and it was Carmel who asked the blunt question: 'Is that allowed? To bury someone, on our land?' Which made Bonaventure stop crying and stand up, and snap that she didn't care if it was allowed, it was happening.

It was clear she herself feared that it would be forbidden.

After she left we sat listening to the silence of the room: the heater thermostat ticking on, the loud hum of the fridge from the kitchen next door, Bonaventure's heavy tread along the lino-leum down the hall and through the rooms beyond. Then Simone said quietly that we should pray, because now all the other obvious problems were rising up in our minds; the border closures and lockdowns, the travel restrictions and all the rest, so rigidly in place once more. But none of us wanted to say any of this to Simone, who looked exhausted, and we all got down on our knees there in the living room and prayed, and I kneeled too and closed my eyes on a picture of muddy bones, clasped in the black roots of a fallen tree.

A POSTCARD ARRIVES from my old colleague Deb: an image of the tall, narrow windows Matisse designed for his chapel in Vence, not long before he died. Deb writes that the gallery in Sydney replicated the chapel with a huge airy white room, and that the coloured seaweed cut-outs of the stained-glass windows reached from floor to ceiling. *I sat in the room for ages and I wished there was such a chapel I could visit,* she writes. She quotes Matisse:

> All art worthy of the name is religious. Be it a creation of lines, or colours: if it is not religious, it does not exist. If it is not religious, it is only a matter of documentary art, anecdotal art . . . which is no longer art.

I briefly fantasise about asking Simone if I can go to see this exhibition, then let the thought fall away as I always do – dropped into the ocean beneath all my urgent, passing desires – and forget about it. I'm touched to hear from Deb again, because she knows I won't reply. Last time I was in contact with her was more than four years ago, on Facebook.

~

I'm going to disappear, my mother would say, meaning she was going into the garden. It was her personal realm, in the way the kitchen or 'the Home' was supposed to be the domain of women at that time. My mother cared little for housework or cooking – although she did plenty of both, by necessity – and would spend as much time as she could outside. When I was older, I wondered if part of the appeal was its legitimising her desire to be alone. She preferred no company, except at times when she needed my father to do some heavy lifting or help with some structural apparatus – making a wooden frame for espaliering fruit trees, perhaps, or drilling metal eyelets into a brick wall for attaching wires for a climber. I would some-times follow her out to 'help', but I quickly grew bored with the weeding jobs she gave me. Her garden was not a place she needed or desired to share. Only once it began to get dark would she come inside in her dirty old purple jumper and shapeless threadbare trousers, scrub her blackened, ridged fingernails under the laundry tap, and then dip a hand into a big tub of Nivea cream. She smelled of hand cream and earth and sweat – an oily, acidic scent I associate with the dandelion flowers we used to call 'wet-the-beds' at school. This was her smell always, I think. She smelled of garden, even when she could no longer go outside.

~

You do not announce on Facebook that you, an atheist, are leaving your job and your home and your husband to join a cloistered religious community. I mean you could, and it might be a better way than I chose, which was not to announce anything to anyone. People were wounded. Very wounded. They told me so in the letters that came for a time in a steady river, to let me know of the hurt and damage I had caused by my disappearance, how much it was still rippling. Alex's letters were not so full of fury, though injury still lay between the lines of his unbearably formal notes about legal things to be resolved. And he would drop in details of his projects – the Guinea mangroves, biodiversity financing, the rest; 'actually making a difference' – to underline his faith, his commitment, my abdication. His hurt was evident, too, in the fact he freely gave the abbey's address to others, despite my asking him not to.

Deb especially had been mystified, then furious. She thought I had more guts, she said, among other things. A later letter, less furious but worse, because her pain was closer to the surface: it wasn't just leaving that was destructive, she wrote, it was the contagion of it, the contempt it showed for her and everyone else at the centre, making fools of them all for keeping at it. Most especially the young ones, she said, whom we *owed*. Some of them wrote too, with more rage even than Deb. I think she encouraged them to do so.

A long time later she sent another note, just defeated and sad. What fundamentally hurt her most of all was my secrecy, not telling her of my 'plans'. But what seemed, still is, impossible to explain was that I didn't plan anything. I came back here one last time and then just . . . didn't go home.

After a while I stopped opening the letters, and then I asked Simone not to give them to me anymore. I knew she did not want to be the keeper of this burden. People who choose this life are not supposed to go around causing such terrible pain to people. It's cruel.

Yet I know this much: everyone here has hurt someone by coming.

I SAW A mouse in the laundry today. Zipped out from under the washing machine, right across my path, to a gap behind the broom cupboard, and frightened the bejesus out of me. It knew its way around that laundry. A tiny grey thing; sweet, pointed little face. But I did not want to see it.

I told the others of this later. When I said 'bejesus' I saw Dolores's eyes widen in disapproval and then she looked quickly at Simone. I had to stop myself making a mocking face back at her. She seems *so* young to me, though she must be nearly twenty-nine now. Still stomps about wearing the same black puffy vest over her tunic, just as when I first saw her. It's her security blanket, and when I think of that I'm filled with sympathy for her and stop feeling mean. She misses her mother, who sends her maudlin letters and photographs of her siblings from Quezon City.

~

Came across Simone's ghastly little back scratcher where she left it, on the arm of the couch. She normally carries it around in her pocket (the tunics have very roomy pockets, I have learned) but sometimes leaves it on a table or a chair, like today. The first time I saw her use it I laughed out loud. It seemed both intimate and a little obscene, as though she were applying underarm deodorant in public. Now it's as ordinary as watching her tie a shoelace. She draws it from her pocket, extends the little stick to its full length with a snap and then dives it down the back of her collar and pokes it around, her elbow jiggling in the air. Sometimes she does this while talking to you, tilting her head and making a little squint of pleasure and satisfaction, scratching away. It's the same expression you see on dogs sometimes. But she keeps talking, eyes fixed on you, not quite closed but screwed up a little.

The silver end of the scratcher is in the shape of a horrible, skinny little *hand*.

~

Bringing in the sheets from the line, I looked down across the paddocks and saw a pelican gliding, landing on the dam. It travelled over the surface for long, long seconds with inches of air between itself and the water before stretching out its legs, leaning back and rowing the air with those enormous, graceful wings.

Also at the line I watched Carmel bend to pick up the great pile of dry sheets in the basket to carry back. Her arms wide open in descent, as if to swoop up a small child.

NOBODY KNOWS WHEN the remains – Sister Jenny's bones – will arrive, or how. The borders are still closed, even for 'essential travel'. It is impossible to get exemptions and, anyway, flights are scarce. Priority is given to returning Australians; living, not dead.

For days now, whenever I have seen Bonaventure at prayer, her poor soft face has been wet with tears.

~

I'm unsure how much this transfer of the bones might be complicated by the fact of Simone's . . . unpopularity, if that is the word for it, with the higher-ups. Some time ago a guest apparently 'reported' her for not being strict enough in the running of the place. She's never said anything about it, but Josephine told me just after it happened; she was the one who saw the complaint email, and the names copied in. She was helping me peel potatoes as she told me this, and hinted that Simone's troublesome laxness included my being allowed to live here. I still don't know if this is true, but I think a part of Josephine enjoyed conveying that impression. We stood side by side, scrubbing the dirt from potatoes, and I let the silence between us lengthen, and I think she did not enjoy that. When I first met Josephine I had the impression of someone quite formidable – because of her height and her face, I suppose, her long nose, and her smooth, confident physicality during the hours in church. But since then I have learned that she is a very timid person. Her face flushes red at any direct question.

At the sink that day I eventually asked her how Simone had responded to this complaint. Her face went even redder and she said Simone had just rolled her eyes and said something dismissive in French. Josephine drew her hands from the dirty water then and wiped them busily on her apron and said she had to go. I think she didn't want me to ask any more questions, though I had not planned to.

It's true that for a couple of weeks after that day Simone went around looking harried, and writing a lot of emails.

~

Last night before bed I made my way outside and stood in the drive to look at the stars in the cold black sky. After so many years of living in cities, the endlessness of the night sky here pours a wild, brilliant vertigo into me.

The lights were soft in the bedroom windows all along the dormitory side as I returned along the gravel path, and I heard my footsteps, I heard a possum scuffling high in the trees, and I was grateful to lead this life here, now.

There may be a word in another language for what brought me to this place; to describe my particular kind of despair at that time. But I've never heard a word to express what I felt and what my body knew, which was that I had a need, an animal need, to find a place I had never been but which was still, in some undeniable way, my home.

~

Early this morning, after my reverie about the stars and the possum, I discovered that something – probably that same possum – had got through not only the poly-tunnel plastic (unsurprising; it is starting to decay) but almost all the pest-proof cloches I'd made for the new hardened-off lettuces, and had eaten almost every plant down to its roots. I swore up to the trees, and then I realised. Not possums – *mice*.

Only three baby lettuces remained. I got to work, pulling apart the cloches that Richard Gittens had shown me how to make from chicken wire and old doorhandles. I doubled the wire layers, dug deeper moats around the plants in which to bury the wire. I kneeled before my tiny green shrines in the dry morning air with the smell of the soil, the cockatoos wheeling and screeching above me, and worked. Heaped up the straw around them, twisted the new cloches deeper into the moats and pressed the surrounding earth into place. Drove the pegs deep into the now-compacted earth with my boot heel. Knowing all of it would likely be futile.

Across the grounds the bell rang for Lauds.

~

My mother used to hold out a heap of garden soil in two cupped hands, marvelling, calling me over to sniff and feel the moist black clumps, to see a pink worm coiling from them. Sometimes it seemed she loved the earth itself more than the plants.

TOWARDS THE END of lunch I opened my mouth to ask about the noise I'd heard in the middle of the night. Had anyone else heard, or had I dreamed, the piano playing itself long after midnight? But before I could ask this, Simone said, surprisingly casually I thought, that Sister Jenny's remains would arrive here in a fortnight. *God willing.*

We all looked down the table at Simone. It seemed she was trying to make this news something ordinary, as if she were talking about the flowers roster or repairing the chicken shed roof (again). She said lightly that 'inquiries' had been going on over the past several weeks, in diplomatic circles and among influential people, and 'progress is being made'. Once the bones are here, and permission is given by the local authorities, Sister Jenny will be laid to rest properly here at the abbey. At this last part Simone was particularly brisk, needing, it seemed, to pass swiftly over what this actually means – over the fact of a grave having to be dug (by whom, where?), and bones lowered into it (by us?). I watched Bonaventure, who breathed quietly, but her expression revealed nothing.

There was quite a bit of work yet to be done – 'administratively speaking' – to get all this happening, Simone said, but a way had been found for the bones to be brought back into the country, accompanied by a returning Australian. Then she stopped speaking and went back to her lunch, and I knew she would not say any more about this today.

I'm used to it now, the waiting. An incomplete, unhurried emergence of understanding, sitting with questions that are sometimes never answered.

~

At first I was struck – a little irritated, honestly – by how slowly the women spoke here, by the long pauses they gave before responding to any question or remark. It seemed affected. But then I recalled a long trip across the country when I was a young woman, driving with my friends from the east coast to the west and back again, twice across the Nullarbor, camping each night along the way. It took a month, and during that month we became slower and slower in our movements. At first we would drive long distances, set up camp in the dusk, rise very early the next day to pack up and move on. But by the end of the trip we would drive only three or four hours a day, and we took longer to do everything. Packed up later and later in the mornings. When at last we drove back into the inner city we were frightened by the speed of everything, by how loudly people spoke. Waiters seemed to be shouting when they came to take your order for dinner.

Alex was one of the people on that trip. We were young, and we would take turns driving and lounging in the back of our friend's car, sometimes singing along to whatever music was playing, but as the trip went on just as often watching the passing skies dreamily for hour on hour. Things were uncomplicated and free, and I don't think I have ever again felt as free as I did on that drive across the desert. Except here. Once or twice here I have felt it.

IT WAS NOT lovely, it was disturbing, to hear the piano in the night for a second time. This time the others heard it too, the first few notes filtering into our dreams. But then I knew that we were all awake, listening to the plinking of those discordant, arrhythmic piano notes in the still, dark night. It was a wrong and menacing sound, like someone drunk or ill collapsing over the keys. I heard Simone open her door and I heard her slippers brushing against the dry boards as she moved down the corridor, turning left at the end of the dormitory-side hall, moving past the kitchen and dining room and into the sitting room. I was fully awake now but unwilling to get out of bed myself. I lay and listened hard, but all that happened was the creak of the piano keyboard lid being opened and loudly closed again, light switches going on and off, and Simone's footsteps returning to her room and the door closing.

~

The smell of distant smoke in the early morning. Richard Gittens confirmed it: the first lightning strike and grass fire of the season, on the other side of the town. They put it out quickly, but still. Summer's here, he said.

~

The bones are to arrive in approximately eight days, we learn, and once they do we will keep a vigil, watching over them – over *her*, Sister Jenny – in the blue sitting room that is properly named Our Lady's Parlour but which has come to be jokingly called 'the good room'. This is named for what Carmel's mother called the living room at the front of their suburban Adelaide house, that room the family was never allowed to enter except when visitors came.

Our vigil, Simone has explained, is to last until the local council completes the burial permission, and then we will hold a proper service and Sister Jenny will be laid to rest in a consecrated place yet to be decided.

There swept over us – over me, at least – a similar feeling of disturbance as that which came over me when I heard the piano in the night. A ghostly feeling of threat, of portent. I shook it off, ashamed, because what could be more human, more natural or tender, than laying the bones of the dead in their rightful home in the earth? But I still felt it.

After Simone told us all this, she picked up her tea mug and took a sip, and then she said the returning Australian who would bring the bones here is Sister Helen Parry. Took another slurp of her tea.

TWO MICE SEEN inside this morning, in the sitting room. Sissy saw a flicker, a speeding blur – long rubbery tail – between piano and bookshelf, and at the very moment she shrieked a second one appeared and sped after the first! I saw her in the hallway immediately afterwards, shuddering and brushing her long pale fingers repeatedly down the front of her tunic as if to wash vermin traces off her body, though of course they'd come nowhere near enough to touch her. But I understood how the sight of them was enough to cause that panicked, violated feeling. Especially for Sissy. I'm not sure exactly why I think it should be worse for her, but it has to do with her delicacy and pale skin, the drifty way she moves (I thought I'd got past her name, which at first seemed *so* absurd, but perhaps that is part of it too). The others, even Josephine, seem hardier to me.

And Simone is a pragmatist, above all. It's one of the reasons I like her so much.

Afterwards came discussion about the problem of what to do. The moral problem of killing them. Because what harm are they doing, simply scurrying about, eating crumbs? In the past the sisters have been lucky with mice – it has always been too cold here for the infestations that move elsewhere across the country from time to time, and a few mice here and there did no harm. The sisters were more careful about securing foods in the pantry, and they let the chickens out more often to chase them around the yards, and nature took its course. But that luxury might exist no longer, it seems: the spring was hotter than ever, and since then it has been drier than usual everywhere, and because of this the mouse plague in the north of the country has begun to spread further south and east than in the past. We have never kept cats here, because of the wildlife. But now Richard Gittens tells us a plague is on the way, and we'd better get ready.

~

We gathered around and braced ourselves as Simone opened the top of the piano. It was empty of creatures, but there was a *nest*. The felt was torn off many of the hammers, and a large soft nest had been made of the felt shreds. Also what looked like

75

kapok stuffing and feathers occupied the centre, spreading in a mound over the hammers and strings. It stank, of course. It was a long time since anyone had played this piano – Josephine prefers to practise on the organ itself in the church. We stood around it, peering in then recoiling at the smell. Simone closed the lid and declared that Richard Gittens was right and our duty now was to 'control' the mice, which meant killing as many as possible. We would find ways to atone.

Later, Richard arrived with a bucket full of bait, some grey plastic mouse traps and boxes of horrifying yellow sticky mats, and Bonaventure emerged from the dark of the old tool shed with half-a-dozen more traps in a dusty cardboard box. But we have not yet laid the bait or set the traps. We prayed about this. Or at least they did, and I . . . thought closely about the mice and what a plague might mean. What would happen if we did nothing? What can we afford to lose, and what must be protected?

Nobody has told Richard Gittens about the coming bones, and what's to be done with them here. We're not to talk about it, even among ourselves. There is to be *no circus*, as Bonaventure puts it. At the time of Jenny's disappearance, apparently, there was news coverage; I don't remember this. I doubt anyone would care these days. But still, what about the council people? I asked. Surely gossip will trickle out. Simone said she would deal with that if it happened, but *we* are to say nothing to anyone. Meaning Richard, our only visitor now.

I suspect Simone's real reason is that if we talk about it with each other, the disturbance will be greater. This is supposed to be a place of refuge, of steadiness. Not agitation.

~

Richard Gittens has no patience for hand-wringing about killing rodents. Looking Simone in the eye after Vespers, he said, 'You have no idea how bad it can get.'

~

I'm afraid of the mice. Such tiny, seemingly defenceless creatures, and yet the sight of even a single one on the verandah, its unafraid plump little body curved there, nibbling and sniffing, sets my heart jolting in fright.

As for Helen Parry . . . To me, this is an even greater shock than the coming of the bones.

I DRIVE INTO town with my usual conflicting feelings. Try not to feel nervous *or* excited at leaving here, but every time, foolishly, I am both. None of the others leave for anything but 'medical appointments or important business'. General errands are left to me.

Before I left, Josephine was sent to the church to mark out a border around the organ with the awful sticky traps. Bonaventure took the bait bucket. Simone looked at me and said, 'You'd better do the kitchen,' and I was grateful. The pantry shelves were indeed dotted with mouse shit, but surprisingly only one large bag of flour was torn open. I am to go into town to find containers – metal and glass – for replacing the plastic tubs holding the rice and beans and spices and other dry goods. Simone called after me: 'No plastic lids, either; they'll eat through them.'

Once I saw a Buddhist nun in a kitchenware shop, looking yearningly at an expensive food processor. I felt smug watching her, thinking, *You poor thing.* Now I sit in the car breathing slowly, trying to calm the buzz in my nerves before going into a charity shop for old jars. Since I came back to live here I have recognised nobody from my youth apart from Richard Gittens, and even he didn't remember me until I reminded him that day on the road. But a strange fear of being recognised accompanies me anyway. I'm masked now (still a novelty for us, while the rest of the country is sick of them), and there is a relief in that anonymity.

I drive out of town with boxes of jars clinking on the back seat.

~

For a brief time when I was a child there was a piano teacher in our town who went from house to house, giving private lessons. He was in great demand because he came from Sydney, he was charming and he had taught music at The Con. I didn't know what The Con was, but the name was spoken with great reverence. After a few months, though, instances began to be pieced together. A filthy joke told to a twelve-year-old boy in one house. In another, the teacher's insistence to a girl's mother that of course she must feel free to pop down to the shops during the lesson. Then the teacher stood behind a boy to correct his posture on the piano stool, and the boy felt something at his back. He did not tell his parents about this, but when it came time for his next lesson he stayed away from home until dark, and his embarrassed mother had to pay the teacher anyway.

My mother told me years later that the police were never called, but that once word got around, the parents told the teacher he'd better leave town quick smart. And he did.

In the car this recollection came, the first time I'd thought of it since childhood. It must have been from seeing the piano lid opened yesterday, all that filth exposed, the stench released into the open at last.

Nobody knew where the piano teacher went next. None of the parents considered telling any authority, and no warnings followed him.

~

When I think about the phases of my life, it is as a series of rooms behind me, each with a door to a previous room left open, behind which is another room, and another and another. The rooms are not quite empty, not exactly dark, but they are shadowy, with indistinct shapes, and I don't like to think about them much. When I hear the name 'Helen Parry', I think of those rooms furthest back, in the deepest shadows.

~

St Ursula's Catholic High School is still there, an old granite building on the hill opposite the church. It was not at all – still is not – a fancy school. We didn't wear hats or blazers, and there were no boarders, as people seemed to expect when I moved to Sydney as an adult and was asked where I'd been educated. It was an ordinary country school, with a few gifted teachers and the rest who trudged through our lessons with little enthusiasm. Who could blame them?

There were a few interchangeable nuns who drifted around St Ursula's – but the only one I remember clearly was Sister Marian, a beaky middle-aged woman who taught religion, naturally, and something else. Geography? I was never taught by Sister Marian, though; by the time I reached the age for her classes she had left the convent to marry a defrocked priest.

The thing I remember about Sister Marian was a howl that came out of her when once, chased by a classmate in some teasing teenage game, I dropped (or half-heartedly threw, I guess) his pencil case out of an upper-storey window. I didn't mean for it to hit Sister Marian, but that is what happened. The very strange thing was that she claimed it had struck her lower abdomen, though this was surely impossible – had she been lying on the concrete? I didn't dispute this, because Sister Marian was shrieking furiously up at the classroom window that her 'chance of motherhood' might have been ruined. What?! We kids laughed and laughed: she was so old, for one thing, but also, we hooted to each other, had she not noticed that *she was a nun*?

This memory I have of Sister Marian is pure and sharp, but surely absurd. A nun complaining of her *womb* being endangered by a falling pencil case! Naturally the other source of our mirth was her ludicrous idea that anyone would ever want to have *sex* with her. And then she left, and we had to adjust our ideas about Sister Marian. Thinking of it now, I wonder how old she actually was.

This was a time of strange outbursts from teachers in that school. We were a badly behaved group of students, it is true. There was a Spanish teacher – a dazed sort of woman who had never learned to discipline a mob – who once broke down in the classroom when one of us whined that some instruction she'd given was not fair. She roared: '*Life is never fair!*' We stared at her. '*Children* can die, at *two years old!*' she wailed, and then she began to sob.

Mrs Teixeira did not have children, we knew; she was another old, plain, strange woman completely unsuited to her job. Is this why we were so cruel to her? The room fell silent, all of us riveted with embarrassment, as she wept. When she finally left the room, breathless with anguish, we broke into cackles, releasing our stifled hysteria. Nobody felt sorry for Mrs Teixeira; we felt only contempt. She really should find another line of work. Yet she was back the next week, as if nothing had happened. I wonder now if any of the other staff even knew of her outburst. Regardless, I doubt anyone helped her. She never became a better teacher, though she stayed for years and years.

Mr Hogan, the headmaster at St Ursula's, was a quiet young man who mostly wore a scuffed brown leather jacket a size too big. He had a clipped ginger beard and an air of tragedy about him because his pretty wife had multiple sclerosis. At school he had an avuncular demeanour and smiled often, showing his neat white teeth. One day at the morning assembly, as we stood yawning and shivering in the weak winter sunlight, he spoke with reverence into the little microphone. 'Girls and boys, I can give you one piece of advice in this life: don't worry about anything; pray about *everything*.'

I thought that was the stupidest thing I had ever heard.

Now, when I drive to and from town, I pass the school on the hill and I remember all these people – the headmaster and his hopeless advice; Sister Marian and her injured womb; poor, hysterical Mrs Teixeira. I never had an ounce of respect for any of them. And here I am, recalling my adolescent cruelty, and feeling sorry.

~

I spend the afternoon in pleasant, rhythmic, mindless industry: scouring off labels, washing jars and lids, sweeping up mouse shit, washing down all the shelves, scrubbing away dust and other ominous stains and blobs in the pantry. Sterilising the jars on oven trays. Cooling them, filling them from the packets and bags of flour, lentils, couscous, spices, seeds and nuts and dried fruit. Writing new labels with felt pen on masking tape. After a few hours I stand back and admire my clean shelves, my shining rows and rows of filled jars.

It would be impossible to explain to anyone from my old life why or how this – whatever it is; servitude? – fills me with such peace.

A CLEANING FRENZY is in progress. Everybody at it, vacuuming and dusting and polishing the whole place, especially the good room, for the bones, which are coming this week – in three days, possibly four. Every week or so there's an update, then a delay, then another expected arrival date is announced. There's a scurrying, excitable feeling among the sisters that keeps leaking out from behind the masquerade of solemnity about the bones. I find myself humiliated, for all of us, by this spinsterish fussing and primping. Yet I am as bad as the rest: I too welcome the frisson of approaching change; I run a damp cloth over the good room windowsills, the mantelpiece, I make the vacuum roar, I scurry around like everyone else.

~

Since learning of the bones and Sister Jenny's saintliness, I've been revisited by Maria Goretti, eleven years old when she was stabbed to death and became a saint. I was ten, in primary school, when Sister Aloysius told this to our class and I fell in love with Maria Goretti.

Maria was stabbed, we learned, because she refused to sin.

There were a lot of numbers in Sister Aloysius's report. Fourteen times Maria was stabbed, with a ten-inch awl, by a man who seemed somehow related to her family, but not really. An awl, we learned, was a long, spiked tool for making holes in things.

On the day of the attack, Maria was sitting on the doorstep in the sunshine, mending the shirt of this not-quite-cousin, Alessandro. Maria was poor and she was Italian. I saw her long lustrous hair, her soft olive skin in the sunlight. I heard this Alessandro calling her inside the house.

Alessandro killed Maria Goretti, Sister Aloysius said, when she refused to commit a Mortal Sin. The refusal was important – but even more important, it seemed, was that as Maria died in hospital, she *forgave her killer.*

I may be imagining now the relish with which Sister Aloysius told us this story. I may be inventing the strange masochistic desire in her voice. But if I am, what then was going through her mind as she told us all of this? Why did she include such gratuitous details? And why did I become so enamoured of

Maria? My first thought is that ten-year-old me loved Maria because she was ordinary. She didn't commune with Jesus or see visions of the Virgin Mary. She just went about her business, a young girl, like us. But there was also a terrible glamour to her story, glimpsed between the lines of Sister Aloysius's words. Maria was desired. A man wanted her. She resisted, ran around the room putting tables between them, but she was doomed. And then celebrated because of her bravery, her resistance. I suspect I ignored the part about forgiveness. It was the chasing and the violence, the drama, that compelled me.

Sister Aloysius had dry white skin and was extremely old. She had a hoarse, throaty voice like an old man's, and a man's big wide hands to slap you on the legs for . . . what? Talking. Laughing. Something you did wrong when you stood in assembly lines in the sun. The pink gravel of the playground was as dry and pale as Sister Aloysius's old skin. The light was so bright it made your eyes water and we had no hats, nobody had hats then for school in an Australian summer, we just squinted. We had grey-and-white cotton school dresses with a fine blood-red thread through the seersucker checks, and little cloth belts with white plastic buckles that always slid crookedly. White Peter Pan collars. White socks, black shoes, bare brown legs for the slapping. All of this now, the innocence of our clothes, our bare children's shins, somehow makes the teacher's telling of Maria Goretti's story worse.

I don't think Sister Aloysius mentioned what I later learned: that Alessandro first tried to choke Maria before he stabbed her fourteen times. I don't think she mentioned that Alessandro had tried to rape Maria Goretti twice before, but she hadn't told anyone because she thought she would get into trouble. I don't think Sister mentioned that Alessandro was twenty. I think she did make clear somehow – without saying it, of course – that because Alessandro did not get his way, St Maria Goretti died a virgin.

Alessandro went to jail. In prison he dreamed that Maria gave him lilies, but they burned in his hands. When he was released from jail twenty-seven years later, he visited Maria's mother and *she* forgave him for killing her daughter, we were told, and they went to mass and took communion together the next day.

By this time Alessandro loved Maria Goretti. He called her *my little saint.*

He became a lay brother and was accepted into a monastery, working in its garden until he died peacefully, of natural causes, at the age of eighty-seven. That was in 1970, only a few years before Sister Aloysius told us the story of St Maria Goretti.

As I grew older I was confused as to why martyrdom was never just called 'murder'. But it was at ten years old I first became confused about the nature of forgiveness, and of atonement, and the conditions under which they could each take place.

~

Living this life, I am convinced, makes a person dream more vividly. Last night: a family of kangaroos, haunch-deep in a quietly lapping tropical ocean, nuzzling at the edges of large floating piles of garbage, eating.

THE MICE HAVE been steadily growing in numbers. We are trapping five or six a day now, but we see even more of them in our peripheral vision, darting across the floor between pieces of furniture, whizzing along the skirting boards.

I have set two traps in the good room, with peanut butter, which we're told is better than cheese.

In the kitchen now, if you set a trap and push it into the gap beside the fridge, it goes off within fifteen minutes. We take turns emptying the traps, releasing the bar (I learn this is called the 'hammer', for obvious grisly reasons) and flinging the limp little bodies either into the chook pen, or over the furthest back garden fence.

We have made 'clean-up kits' and stationed them along the halls and verandahs: buckets containing boxes of disposable latex gloves, spray bottles of disinfectant, wads of paper towel and rags.

As yet the traps in the good room remain unsnapped. They sit there, little grey plastic sentries on each side of the door, awaiting our visitor. The peanut butter hardening over the days.

~

I had a childhood friend whose father owned the Holden dealership in town. 'Owned' might be an overstatement; I think now that he must have been merely its manager, for his name appeared nowhere in connection with the place, and he seemed to enjoy none of the status attached to other car-dealer men in town. The large signs for other car yards were boldly patriarchal: VIC THOMPSON & SONS AUTOMOTIVE, which sold Fords, or RAY BEVERLEY TOYOTA.

My friend lived with her father in a tiny house behind the car showroom. The house – a sort of demountable cabin really – was an airless box with two tiny bedrooms, low white-tiled ceilings and small aluminium sliding windows of the kind normally only seen in bathrooms. I only noticed the windows particularly because my mother – who was not snobbish about much – had an aversion to aluminium windows that was never explained but which I thought was to do with people who were somehow uneducated, or poor. I did not tell her about the windows, nor that on the weekends my friend's father would watch television in his underpants, while drinking beer from a glass tankard otherwise kept in the freezer. My own father drank cheap red wine from cardboard casks, and I had only ever seen his underpants and singlet as he made his way to or from the shower. Although I was afraid at the sight of my friend's father's fleshy thighs, his hairy belly exposed, he was not exactly threatening. It was more as if he didn't notice whether his daughter was there or not. She was an exceedingly quiet child. He never spoke to her, or to me, when I was there.

Mostly she and I played in the showroom after closing time, sliding around the linoleum floors in our socks, and lying in the cars talking and laughing softly, with the seats reclined and the doors and boots all open, the cars smelling new and clean, glossy as insects, wings extended.

In the stuffy box house my friend kept pet mice in a bird-cage lined with newspaper. They were small and white or light grey, with pointed faces and pink eyes. She would slide up the small birdcage door and bring her cupped hand down hard over one soft body and draw it out, squirming and then still. She held it so tight sometimes I thought it was dead. She asked me if I wanted to hold it but I never did. Then she would push her fist back through the door and release the creature, which writhed from her grip and scampered to the far side of the cage.

Soon the mice had babies – awful, long bald slugs – and then those babies quickly had more babies. Her house smelled of mice, and I have recognised even the faintest whiff of it immediately, anywhere, ever since.

When there were too many babies, which happened very quickly, my friend took the birdcage into the scrubby bare block across the road from the dealership and opened the cage door. We watched the mice spill out and scatter into the dry grass. In an instant they had gone. The birds and the cats would get them, her father said. Nobody seemed upset. What was the appeal of a mouse as a pet? My friend never let them run up her sleeve or sit inside her collar, like you saw happen on TV occasionally. Nor did the mice have names. She didn't appear to like them much; she just kept them trapped in the cage, and then let them all go at once.

Next she had a single guinea pig, which I found almost as repellent as the mice. I hated to hold it, with its shivering delicate body and tiny claws when she plonked it into my lap, but at least it was allowed to live outside, in a metal cage. She would thrust handfuls of grass at the guinea pig, and then let the heavy lid of the cage fall shut.

Even after the mice had long disappeared from the house, the odour inside remained, and I have always associated that smell with the father in his underpants, the quiet daughter, the unmentioned misery of divorce.

DOLORES DRIVES ME mad with her constant sneezing and scratching. I order myself not to be annoyed: the girl can't stop herself having hay fever! But her sneezing is so *operatic*. She can be heard from across the courtyard, through walls, on and on, and then she traipses around leaving crumpled tissue crumbs as she goes, her red eyes streaming. But it's the full-body convulsions I can't stand; the dramatic pause, the way she casts her pitiful gaze around at anyone in the room, before another round of swooping, high-performance noise, then the little moans as she scrubs at her face with tissues. The crackle of antihistamine blister packs follows her around.

Sometimes I think this place is sending me insane. I fill with disgust at my own pettiness, punish myself by being extra nice to Dolores in small ways. Picking up her damn puffy vest from the floor for the millionth time.

Really I just want to say to her, You're so young. Go away from here, go home to your mother and your sisters. Go to their weddings, hold their babies. *Live.*

THERE WAS A girl at my high school whose mother used to hit her with the kettle's electrical cord. I'm not sure how we knew this, because this girl was entirely friendless; an outcast. In whom could she possibly have confided?

The girl and her mother – there was no father – lived in a housing commission flat in the town, in an ugly red-brick block with vacant land on either side. There were no houses nearby; only, further along the road, a service station and the Lutheran church (who or what was a Lutheran? we never found out). No trees or shrubs softened the air around the block, there was no shelter from weather or inspection by passers-by. There was a cement driveway and a couple of faded-looking cars, but the girl's mother did not have a car. She was the only mother we ever saw catch the school bus, and this was a degrading sight. Watching the girl's mother climbing the bus stairs with her bags of groceries was like seeing someone naked. This same mother – an angry, frightening woman – was said to abandon her daughter at times, going away and leaving the girl to care for herself for weeks and weeks at a time.

I don't remember the moment I learned about this girl's outcast status. It had simply always been known that she was bad: a loud, unruly girl, repellent to all. I could never understand why she did not just try to shut up and fade into invisibility, for she was constantly punished by teachers and taunted by her classmates, but she seemed unable to submit. There was something threatening in the way she appeared not to notice the detentions and taunts and insults, and though we never spoke of it, I think it was this power that frightened all of us, and made her hateful.

Occasionally – not very often – I felt pity for her apparent inability to understand the basic rules of survival. She would walk up to a group of girls in the playground, for example, and ask a question or, worse, give an opinion: on a girl's sneakers or schoolbag or jacket. Worst was when she gave compliments, for praise from this girl was an insult, and the recipient would be teased for months. *I like your hair, Leanne*, we'd mimic in our stupid, nasal voices, while Leanne cringed and begged us to stop.

This girl had sandy blonde hair that she wore in crooked plaits – we decided her hair was dirty, and her teeth, too, seemed grubby and misaligned. My own teeth were also crooked, and I had many other defects, but unlike the girl I'd learned to hide them as best I could or, failing that, at least had the grace to be ashamed of my big nose and my thin hair, my flat chest and hipless figure. I wore my uniform as unremarkably as possible – shapeless and with enough length to go unnoticed, but not foolishly baggy like poor Julie Gower, harmless but annoying, her uniform ballooning around her like a long pale green tent. Most of us, let's face it, knew our place in the pecking order (even Julie Gower), and stayed there.

This girl, though, as well as being loud, wore her uniform tight and very short, and her breasts developed too early. Someone claimed to know that she had got her first period at age eleven, which was disgusting, a fact that spoke to her general vulgarity. On the girl the tight short tunic looked more like poverty than sex, but that was there too, animal and fierce.

Occasionally, watching the girl across the playground accosting some other girl (or boy – she was incapable of coy dissembling in the presence of boys, another mark against her), my group of friends would discuss what it would take for her to make herself attractive. This conversation was conducted as a form of charity; we felt good about ourselves at such moments. The girl had a good body, for starters – as if she didn't know;

we rolled our eyes – with long brown legs, a strong waist, finely muscled arms. Even her face, with her little snub nose and full lips, could be sort of okay if she tried. If she would only wash and brush her hair properly, grow out that fringe (was it possible her stupid mother even cut her hair?), change her nasal, grating voice and lower her volume. She did appear to shave her legs, which was something. But there was the problem of her acne, which she did nothing about. This was a delicate subject, as Eleanor, one of our group, was burdened by terrible red patches of severe acne on her face and chest. But Eleanor tortured herself with hours of attention to her pimples: countless applications of flesh-coloured Clearasil and horrible-smelling antibacterial washes, and she never, *ever* touched her skin with unclean hands. Whereas the girl – we could tell – picked and squeezed and allowed her skin to become infected. She never once looked clean. Which, it went without saying, was the greatest possible teenage-girl sin.

During these sessions we would piously suggest to each other the many possible ways the girl could improve her appearance and thereby avoid some of the social wounds she suffered. And then we would sigh, because this girl didn't even *want* to look nice or fit in or be liked – some people just don't want to be helped – and this freed us then to go back to hating her. The boys did most of the really horrible things, the physical and sexually humiliating things, but we girls laughed when they did them, and elsewhere chimed in with our own sweetly offered savagery (*Are you using new gel in your hair*, we would ask her innocently, *or is that just natural greasiness?*).

Every Thursday, when the boys did woodwork or metalwork and other girls did home economics, some of us took sewing classes with Mrs Bird, whom we adored. We would always try to impress Mrs Bird because Mrs Bird was not a teacher, and nor was she even Catholic. She was elegant and calm and wry and smart, and spoke to us as if we were almost adult. Faced with some stupid school regulation – about wearing ties, or no badges allowed on bags – Mrs Bird would sigh and shake her head, and then appeal to us with a raised eyebrow, asking us to humour her so she wouldn't get into trouble about enforcing these silly rules. We did with enthusiasm whatever Mrs Bird asked. She was so *nice*. She would fix our sewing machine blunders for us, compliment our crude work with what seemed like genuine admiration.

One day Mrs Bird had to leave the room on some errand, and while she was absent, something happened with the girl I have mentioned, who was in our class that day.

Afterwards, nobody seemed to know how it had begun, but within moments of Mrs Bird leaving the room there erupted a ferocious brawl, with the girl at the centre. Along with everyone else I leaped into the fray and tried my best to get a few pushes or blows in through the shrieking mob surrounding her. When

I withdrew my hand it seemed someone – the girl! – had bitten it, and *drawn blood*. I held up my hand in triumph.

Then Mrs Bird opened the door. Her cry stilled us all. We fell back to reveal the girl, with her uniform torn and one of her plaits undone. She was not crying. She wiped her nose with her hand, panting and sweating like a cornered animal. Which, in those moments, was what she had been. Mrs Bird stared at us in horror and disbelief, and this was unbearable to us. She stood, speechless with fury, and slowly looked around the room, forcing each of us to meet her gaze, where we saw a terrible hurt. Then, in a quiet, dreadful voice, she told us she had never seen such an appalling display of savagery, and she hoped she never would again. In fact, she said, the lesson was over. We were to pack away our sewing things and wait there, *in silence.*

She stepped across the room to the girl. 'Come with me, Helen,' she said tenderly – her only kindness, for Helen Parry! – and together they left the room. Helen, pulling her dress down, wiping her face, seemed as stunned as the rest of us.

We waited in that airless room in silence, arms folded, flushed with indignation, casting accusing looks around for who had started it – Helen, of course, but who else? When Mrs Bird returned it was with the headmaster, Mr Hogan. Helen, it seemed, had been *driven home* by the *school secretary*! Mrs Bird appraised us, in our rows, with great sadness and disgust. 'You can give your explanation to Mr Hogan,' she said – sombre, dignified. 'I'm not interested.' And she picked up her handbag and left our school.

Mr Hogan waited for Mrs Bird to close the door, listened for her footsteps and the closing of the door at the bottom of the stairs, and then – of course – took our side against Helen Parry. The suggestion of an apology to Helen never arose; the idea that we, or even the school, might seek her forgiveness didn't occur to us. Nobody was punished; we were merely told not to allow the girl to provoke us in such a way again. As the bell went for the next lesson I showed Mr Hogan my hand, which had begun to swell around the bite mark. Blood poisoning, he said without surprise, and sent me to the office for some antiseptic ointment.

Mrs Bird did not come back for three weeks, but by the time she returned – brusquer, less loving – Helen Parry had left our school for good.

SISSY MADE A declaration at lunch today, to nobody in particular. 'God *does* answer prayer,' she said. 'Maybe not always the way we want Him to, but He does answer prayer and He does listen.' She looked around the table, as if expecting applause or at least agreement, but nobody said anything. She pressed on: 'Even if someone is not cured from a terminal disease or something, they might be more at peace.'

I ate in silence, grateful for its protection, because all I ever want to do with Sissy is argue. But I felt a pang for her, because I think she was rehearsing for when Helen Parry arrives. She's defending herself – all of us? – from Helen's scornful assessment. And maybe she's right, about a prayer's answer being not what you want but what you need.

While I chewed I considered Sissy's need to control other people's beliefs, to point out their wrongness, and her need at the same time for them to be grateful for her correction. Like all of us, she does not like to be corrected herself.

When the film actor David Gulpilil died, for a period after his death to use his surname was a grave offence to his culture. Surprisingly it seemed the media had largely respected this custom, and when Simone mentioned David in our week's prayers she too followed this rule. But Sissy was resistant to this. For days she walked around asking, 'But David *who*?' in an irritated way, even though she knew. I ignored her, but more than once I had to leave the room to stop my anger rising and spilling out of me. After a time, Simone simply said sharply: '*Sissy, give it up.*'

Around that time Simone let us watch television one evening – rare – because she wanted us to see a documentary about the actor. What I remember is the tremendous authority of the man, the immense self-respect: 'I don't have to act,' he said. 'I just stand there – and the camera sees me.' Of attending a British royal reception: 'That's when the Queen of England met me.' There was nothing boastful in these observations; he was just remarking on the natural truth of things. He spoke mildly of his cancer, the holes in his lungs that could not be fixed by medicine. And I remember how Sissy's fingers were already fondling her rosary when Gulpilil gazed through the camera lens, through the television screen, when he looked straight into the hearts of all of us in our sitting room and said placidly: 'You can pray for me, but it won't work.' An almost sympathetic smile, stating an unfortunate fact: 'It doesn't work.'

I remember that afterwards, as we put away the teacups, Sissy could not resist the last word. 'He was a smoker, wasn't he?'

There have been many other moments with Sissy since then, but that was the first time I felt hatred in this place. It broke my heart to feel it, although of course I knew these feelings had to be possible – inevitable? – here as out there, in the world. I hoped it would pass. I resolved to stay out of Sissy's way after that, as much as I could.

But today I felt sorry for her. I knew it was Helen Parry's approach and even poor dead Sister Jenny's – these disobedients – causing her to deliver her pious little speech. Nobody else has said anything, but already the place is shivering with self-consciousness, fearing the insinuation we should be something other than we are.

As we sat there chewing in the silence, a crow called outside: *Aaah, aaah, aaaah.*

~

Simone very tetchy today. She shut herself in the office most of the day, apparently going through the procedures for the interment of the bones. No private burial is allowed without a 'development consent' from our local council. There are rules about the grave's proximity to domestic water supply, the size of the property, fencing to prevent damage by 'livestock etc.', legal access and right-of-way considerations if the property is sold. An inspection of the proposed site must be carried out by council's environmental health surveyor. But the council does not appear to have an environmental health surveyor, and now council staff are working from home and nobody is answering the phones. A map showing the exact location of the burial is to be provided. A copy of the death certificate – still to be obtained, somehow, from Thai authorities, despite the imminent release of the remains – must be provided. No special treatment, no exception to the rules for a disappeared, murdered, disinterred nun whose friends simply want to lay her bones to rest. Whose friends want only to visit her grave, tend its garden, kneel there beside her and smooth the grasses over her body.

~

My mother was Catholic by birth, but she was open to certain . . . unorthodox beliefs. Unlike almost everyone we knew, she had an inclination to the mystical, I suppose you could say. Once, a strange friend of hers engaged the services of a water diviner and my mother took me along with her to watch this ancient art take place. We trailed around the paddocks with my mother's friend, some distance behind the man with the sticks. He looked disappointingly ordinary. He dressed more like the engineers my father worked with (tailored shorts and a pressed short-sleeved shirt, with work boots and khaki socks the exception to the office uniform) than any kind of sorcerer. I had expected Catweazle, but this scout leader of a man stamped about the dry paddocks holding out his sticks and glowering. The sound of trucks on the highway floated to us across the land, along with the high whizz of the grasshoppers' song. I think he found it irritating to be watched, and he didn't find any water. But he was unembarrassed: it only proved there was no water to be found.

Another time, when I was about eleven, and after I had long complained of a mysterious pain in my calf muscles I called 'tight legs' and which others, including our family doctor, dismissed lightly as growing pains, my mother took me to someone she referred to as 'a different sort of doctor'. He worked in a room adjacent to a dental surgery in a small building with green-glass bricks in the waiting room, next to the town library. I think now he must have been a reiki prac-titioner, for his treatment consisted of sitting me in a chair and moving about, rubbing rapidly at the air around my body with his two opened hands. There was something I didn't like about the man. He seemed not to see me, and he spoke about me to my mother as if I couldn't hear him, or as if I were a dog, some creature who could not understand language. Once I was seated on a vinyl chair, the man stood over me. My mother looked out of the window, looped her handbag over her shoulder and told me she would be back in a moment, that she wanted to pick up some milk from the corner shop. I could see the shop through the window, and would have been able to watch her the whole time until she returned, but I did not want her to leave me in this room with the man. I would never have been able to say this, but she saw my face, and she sat down again and let the handbag loops slip back into her lap.

'Actually, it doesn't matter,' she said, picking up a magazine.

The man had noticed my expression, and as he stepped around my chair he said to my mother, 'Ah, bit of a crybaby, is she?'

My mother took a moment to meet his eye and then said, her voice very cool, 'Not at all.'

The treatment took about twenty minutes. I sat, embarrassed and alert in the chair, while my mother pretended to read the magazine but actually watched the man carefully as he stepped from side to side, his hands dabbing at the air around my torso, my shoulders and head. Most of the time he was behind me, and I kept my gaze fixed on the leg of my mother's chair. When it was done, I was allowed to peel myself from the sticky vinyl seat, and my mother paid the fee. The man said several more treatments would be necessary, and my mother said she would be in touch about another appointment, but we never went back. We didn't speak of it after that day.

My mother trusted me, and I trusted her.

The tightness in my calves came and went, but eventually I forgot about the pain, so it must have subsided some time in my teenage years.

As I grew into my twenties, then thirties, and learned about other mothers – the complications and layers of hurt and mistrust, of envy and control, and about the confusion so many of my friends still carried about who was parent to whom – I began to understand how rare such a simple and powerful trust had been. I wished again that I had been able to say any of this to her when she lived. Yet I doubt I would ever have said it. There was a quiet but potent aura of unknowability around my mother, and I think now that to say such things would have felt like an impertinence.

~

I have sometimes thought it wrong of me to be so preoccupied with my mother and not my father. But at the same time

I understand why: my father and I *knew* each other, absolutely. And I am convinced that had he lived a long life, I would never have known him more completely than I did as a child. I don't know why that should make such a difference, but it does.

ANOTHER DELAY. AND more mice.

There's an emerging, though unspoken, feeling that Helen Parry herself is to blame for the tension beginning to rise up here – about the bones, even about the mice – for she is a woman known to cause trouble wherever she goes. In everything I've seen, from my time in the forest all those years ago and from observing her in the media over the decades since, Helen Parry comes across as cold, lacking self-scrutiny, and immensely powerful. She is known for her intimidating gaze, and also a strangely flirtatious manner when challenged. Something ruthless and sexual emanates from her. In another era, if she wasn't a nun, she'd be called *a man-eater*. Except her erotic charge is not directed only at men.

Bonaventure calls her 'that celebrity nun' and is not at all happy about her coming. We are to clean her room and make her bed. This seems reasonable to me but not to Bon, who is stomping and huffing about the place. (I feel this is a form of jealousy about Helen Parry's accompanying Jenny's bones on their journey here.) 'She was *my friend*,' Bonaventure has said many times about Sister Jenny, so emphatically it makes me think there is something beneath it, some hurt that is separate from the disappearance or the death.

AT FIRST, WHEN the radical environmentalist nun arrived at the forest camp, I was shaken at hearing another person called that name so coloured by my cloudy adolescent guilt. And when I saw it was indeed her – how on earth had *Helen Parry* become a *nun*? – I tried to hide myself among the others. I lay awake in my sleeping bag remembering those high school years, rigid with shame. She didn't even notice me, of course, but after a few days I could no longer bear the tension, the looming certainty of recognition, denunciation. So I went to her and asked to speak with her for a moment.

My guts churned as she stepped away from the group to stand opposite me, and I waited for recognition to register in her face when she looked at me, but there was none. I told her my name: still none. Helen Parry blinked at me, arms crossed below her breasts, as I told her that we had been at school together, and I wanted to apologise for the way she had been treated.

She frowned. She seemed confused.

I could feel heat in my face when I said, 'There was a sewing class once . . .' and waited, panicked, for her to react.

Still she looked mystified, as if I were talking about someone else, and as though she could not understand why a stranger should so intimately confess some historical crime against a person unknown to her.

I was taken aback by this. She could not have forgotten. I kept going; I told her that I was to this day ashamed of what we had done, and that I was deeply sorry for my part in it. Her unreadable brown eyes watched me as I spoke, and then I saw that she did remember; the brutality of that day opened up behind her eyes.

'Oh, that,' she said, and she sent a strange, ironic smile upwards to the treetops. When her gaze returned to mine I saw a bitter, mocking pity there. For me, which shocked me. We stood in the forest in the silence that lay between us now. What I saw next is what I remember most clearly: a moment's pure agony appeared in Helen Parry's face, and I saw that this pain was not caused by me or even by what had happened in our sewing class that day, but by some other, larger thing. She paused, looking hard at me now. 'I can see why that might have been a big . . . incident . . . for you.' The pitying smile returned, then hardened. 'But for me, that day was nothing.'

And she walked away from me, back to the camp.

So I have watched her, from a distance, ever since. In the decades since that long-ago logging protest, she has slept in tree tents in the Tarkine, filmed illegal whaling from the Sea Shepherd. She has stood up to dictators – Bolsonaro, Duterte – and been imprisoned. She has demonstrated for sex workers' rights in India, for democracy in Hong Kong, and now protests with students in Bangkok. Where Helen Parry goes, journalists follow, lawyers line up to do pro bono work for her. She's suing Australia's government over refugee detention and climate inaction. She's restless, rangy, has her hair shorn almost to a crewcut, wears jeans and a big fat wooden cross around her neck on a string of old hippie beads. At least, she used to.

What struck me in the forest, and does now, is how nothing appeared to have changed in Helen Parry; how the things we schoolgirls so hated her for were exactly the qualities that now gave her such unsettling power. The unashamed demand for space. The way her clothes sat on her body, the animal carnality of her. Her unwavering, absolute readiness for a *fight*.

I have never forgotten that strange feeling, left standing there in the wilderness with my regret and my remorse still around me, suspended in the air. Not denounced, not forgiven. It made me admire her, if I am honest, this refusal to alleviate my discomfort. It made me wonder what forgiveness actually is, or means. What was it that I wanted from her that day?

The way she remained utterly herself, hiding nothing, this made me admire her too. And now that she's coming here, into our silence, it also makes me afraid.

BONAVENTURE HAS BEEN agitated all morning, stabbing into corners with her straw broom, muttering resentfully. There's mouse shit everywhere, fresh each day. I told her I didn't think Helen Parry would care about a bit of mouse shit, given all the filthy places she's slept in her time, and Bonaventure snapped that she didn't care *what* Helen Parry thought, it had nothing to *do* with her. And then she swung around with the broom so vigorously she knocked a little plaster statue of Our Lady off the mantelpiece and it fell to the floor and scattered in broken pieces. Bonaventure made an agonised sound. I told her I would clean it up and took the broom from her. Please, I said, and poor Bon knew she'd been unreasonable all week, and she looked wounded, mortified, before letting go the broom and leaving the guest cabin.

I shoved the broom head under the bed to sweep out the broken pieces of the Virgin, and found that in fact only the head had come off, though the body was chipped in places. I propped it back on the mantel. The statue is familiar from every classroom and church alcove of my childhood. The white tunic with golden belt, the sky-blue flowing veil with its gold edging, two outstretched arms and pink hands. Two pink bare feet (poorly rendered – one significantly larger than the other, and both too large for the body's proportions), one of which presses down on the neck of a spotted snake with its red mouth wide open, forked tongue curling out.

I took a similar statue from my own room and swapped it for the one in Helen Parry's quarters. I put the Blessed Virgin's head beside the broken body on my windowsill and forgot about it. When I came into the room later to pull down the blind I saw Mary's head on its side, her blank bored face gazing into the serpent's open mouth at her feet.

~

Simone saw me at the tall glass-fronted 'library' in the sitting room, looked at the book in my hand and snorted. 'You know there are good books in those shelves, don't you?' I did know. Dorothy Lee, Edith Stein, Joan Chittister, Simone Weil, Ariel Burger. Arendt, Nussbaum, Hitchens, Robinson, Merton. But

Simone had caught me engrossed in *Stories of the Saints*. A children's book, I suppose – or, if not, a book compiled by or for a simpleton. The stories are fantastical, infantile.

St Brigid, for instance. When she was a baby, according to the book, she vomited up the food an old druid gave her because he was impure. A red cow with white ears turned up instead, and fed her. Why did I choose Brigid as my confirmation saint? I don't think I knew about the vomiting or the cow; I was under the impression she just helped the poor. Learned too late that my classmates had chosen their saints based on how the name sounded with theirs. (Heather Hibberd chose St Jessica, one of those who found Jesus' empty tomb, which even then seemed to me an outrageous cheat.)

Mostly the saint stories are of cheerfulness, benevolence, threats, tests of character, followed by torture and maiming. Like St Julia: 'born of noble parents in South Africa', then captured by barbarians who conquered her city. Sold as a slave to a pagan merchant, Julia – the story says – never once complained or felt sorry for herself. She accepted all her punishments as God's will and performed the lowest duties with 'marvellous joyfulness'. One day the Governor became angry when Julia would not take part in a pagan festival, because she loved Jesus. The Governor tried to buy her, but her master refused to sell. Then the Governor offered to set Julia free if she would make one little sacrifice to the pagan gods, but Julia refused, because she loved Jesus. So the Governor ordered someone to strike her face and tear the hair from her head, says the book. Then she was hung on a cross until she died. Her feast day is May twenty-third, which is also my birthday.

I flipped through to find Bonaventure, 'a holy teacher, Italian bishop and doctor of theology': patron saint of bowel disorders, having suffered a life-threatening gastrointestinal illness as a child. One hundred and sixty years after his death, Bonaventure's body was dug up to be moved to a fancier church. When he was exhumed, his head was discovered to be 'entirely incorrupt': St Bonaventure's hair, lips, teeth and tongue showed no sign of decomposition and were perfectly preserved.

I don't think I will show this to Bon.

Something in the voice and the gullible nonsense of these stories recalls *Ten Thousand Dreams Interpreted*, an old book I once found in a charity shop and kept because it amused me. It was a dictionary of objects and concepts ('knife', for example, or 'failure') that supposedly often appeared in dreams, followed by a short declaration of what each foretold for the dreamer. A great many of the entries had a certain meaning, but a different meaning if 'a young woman' dreamed of them. I still remember some – I used to recite them at dinner parties. Tadpoles indicated 'unease in business'. But if a young woman dreamed of tadpoles 'in clear water', it foretold that she would 'form a relation with a wealthy but immoral man'. To dream of salt was an omen of discordant surroundings. But a young woman eating salt in a dream meant her lover would desert her for a more beautiful girl, 'causing her deep chagrin'. My favourite was this: 'To dream of a dolphin indicates your liability to come under a new government. It is not a very good dream.'

THIRTEEN MICE TODAY. A record. We have to do something else about disposing of the bodies. We've been flinging them over the back fence, behind the pine trees into the paddock. But they're piling up and the stench is worsening. We need to be rid of them, to bury or destroy them. Not just because of the smell, but because the simple fact of them is so horrifying.

~

The oven has stopped working. Simone mentioned this to Richard Gittens after Lauds because she was nervous about the electrician's call-out fee, and he told her it would be the mice. The oven will be overheating because they've eaten the insulation. This had happened in his sister's kitchen up north, he said.

He was right. We pulled out the stove and found the insulation torn up and a nest in the box just under the burners, the insulation mixed with hair and threads, littered with edges of biscuits and a chocolate wrapper from who knows where. Sissy was on her knees with rubber gloves and a surgical mask all afternoon, pulling out the insulation and cleaning up the mouse shit and other rubbish before we pushed the stove back.

~

In high school Richard Gittens was a sleepy-eyed, freckled, curly-headed farm boy with a dry, slow sense of humour, though he didn't speak much. I sat next to him in maths class once, and had forgotten my pencil case. I asked him if I could borrow a pen. He feigned reluctance, slowly shaking his head as he passed me one, and said, 'There's a *drought* on, you know.' When I laughed out loud, he blushed and couldn't stop a secret smile at his workbook.

Now and then I remember that time, and I remember too that years later I looked up as I walked behind my mother's coffin being carried from the church, and was surprised to see Richard Gittens, head bowed, in a pew near the back. He didn't come to the house afterwards, and if I hadn't happened to see him I would not have known he was there that day.

After I'd come to stay here, I met his LandCruiser once out on the road on the return leg of my early morning run, after Vigils and before Lauds. He stopped to see if I wanted a lift. I got into his passenger seat and as I buckled my seatbelt I told him my name, and said we had been at high school together. He frowned, confused for a moment, then broke into a smile of recognition. 'Ha! Yes! We were!' he said. And then, as he drove along the pale road in the early sunlight, the flat golden plains spreading out on either side of us, he said: 'Huh.' Meaning, I think, that he would not have expected to see me back here. But I liked that he didn't ask me any questions about it.

Since that day I have thought of Richard as my friend, though I have no idea if he feels the same way. But he has occasionally helped me with the chook shed, or with some particularly heavy work in the garden. He arrives, works in his methodical way, ignores any word of thanks, and leaves.

Decency is the word I think of when it comes to him.

THE SWEET, DOPEY-FACED boy at the hardware store told me electronic payments weren't possible. He held up a cable in his fist to show me: eaten through. I bought as many skeins of steel wool as I could with the cash I had, and we spent today pushing it into every gap we could find between the floorboards and the walls.

Now the oven is unusable we are eating a lot of pasta, or cooking outdoors on the seldom-used barbecue, which creates the strange feel of a holiday. Carmel wound a length of steel wool around the tubing from the gas cylinder to stop the mice eating that.

~

Josephine is revolted because she saw one of the chickens gobbling down a mouse. I've seen this too, from time to time. One of the larger birds, usually – the black one, or the old ISA Brown who somehow came to be called Kitty. I've seen a squirming mouse dangling from her beak, feathers fluffing as she ran in crazed zigzags to escape the others, darting into a corner where they couldn't reach her. She'd whacked the mouse's soft body back and forth on the hard dirt, grabbed at it again, and then it was only the grey tail you saw dangling as she downed it in one or two convulsions, gaze fixed in concentration, forcing down the twitching furry lump. Afterwards, staring and breathing into stillness, opening her beak and closing it in shock, or triumph.

This morning Josephine flung the plastic chook bowl into the sink and shuddered. 'I did not need to see *that*.' And her hand came up involuntarily but then she noticed it, and did not make the sign of the cross after all. (She told me once of the incessant crossing and whispering of the old nuns in her Yeppoon boarding school. She thought them superstitious peasants. She prefers intention, consciousness – yet her hand rises unbidden every other day.) Instead she took out a handkerchief and rubbed her long rosy nose.

I told Josephine, better a chicken eating a mouse than a rat eating a baby chick, which has happened before. Or a goanna, hulking its way into the yard through a break it has forced in the wire. I saw it once. I heard the noise first and ran to see what was upsetting the chickens – and could only watch that prehistoric granite-coloured creature scrabbling, astonishingly quickly, up the wooden post supporting the nesting boxes. Chickens screeching and scattering in all directions across the yard and around the church as the lizard broke open and ate all the new-laid eggs. Then it clambered down in a slow, leisurely way, inspecting the chicken yard as it moved, making sure no eggs had been missed. Only then did it make its way off into the bush once more.

I mended the hole in the fence but it came back twice more before I asked Richard Gittens to help me capture it. He took it away in a feral cat trap and later told me he'd set it free in a stand of bush near the creek on his place.

Carmel claimed that Richard Gittens probably shot it, but I don't believe he would do that. I think she said it because she doesn't approve of my friendship with him. I used to care about what she and the others thought of me over one thing or another, but I don't anymore.

~

I have been trying to see this place once again with a stranger's eyes, to imagine what Helen Parry might make of it. What did *I* make of it when I arrived back then? A worthless raggedy triangle of little paddocks out on the barren plains, wedged between the paintball place, the solar farm, the Gittenses' and the old riding school that once called itself an 'equestrian resort'. The horse-place sign is blistered with age but I believe there are still a few bony old ponies to ride along the stony tracks, and some grim-looking cabins dotted about. But even when the cabins were new, to speak the word 'resort' out loud around here would have been laughable.

(I was taken horseriding once or twice as a kid, and hated it. The sun boiling the sky white while you sat stiffly on a skinny old pony, led about by a teenage girl in grimy jodhpurs and scuffed riding boots, hair in a ponytail, wafting the flies from her face with her murky pink nails. The horse swaying heavily beneath you; clutching the reins so tight your fingernails dug into your palms. The girl would occasionally turn to ask, 'You right?', and you'd nod solemnly beneath your helmet, stiff with embarrassment. Relief for everybody when it was over. When I think of horseriding now, I think of the dust, my simultaneous terror of and sorrow for the huge captive animal, and the raging itching of my eyes swollen into scrunched, puffy balls.)

Passing traffic on our road is rare, except for the weekend minibuses full of young men that trundle past our turn-off on their way to the paintball park. If they happen to see one of us, the paintballers stare out of the bus windows, round-eyed as aquarium fish, and a little later a few hoots and bellows will be heard floating across the paddocks.

Just before the turn-off to our place, Helen Parry will see the drab little clapboard hall, brought down by lorry from the mountains in the seventies and set down on a concrete slab. Back in the fifties it had been a temporary Anglican church for the workers on the Snowy Hydro scheme. Once, the Queen and Prince Philip attended a service in it, but only two dozen parishioners could fit inside so the crowds and the photographers remained out in the sharp cold sunshine, a loud-speaker broadcasting the sermon from within. For a while in the 1960s the little hall was used as an Institute of Arts and Letters for the area's farmers. I have no idea what went on there. Now it's derelict, like most things around here.

Looks are not everything, though. The paintball place, apparently, rakes it in.

THE BONES AND Helen Parry are on their way here. Today.

~

In the night I dreamed of a garden party. Someone had for sale a small velvet-lined box containing a collection of tiny fossils: each one an entire, perfectly formed, minuscule dinosaur in a different delicate colour. A pterodactyl, a tyrannosaurus, an iguanodon and others. Before I could ask the price – I wanted to buy them very much – a child upended the box and spilled the tiny fossils into the rich green lawn. I fell to my knees in silence, desperately searching the grass for the creatures before the loss was discovered.

~

This afternoon, a large black hearse slid into the drive and parked. Three reverential funeral directors from Sydney climbed out of the car and stood in their dark suits in the bright sunlight. It was startling at first to see the row of black masks, but then we remembered. I think they, in turn, were shocked to see us without them.

They opened the back of the hearse and drew out a folding steel trolley, flicked down its legs and then expertly slid onto this a small, plain, brown wooden casket. They snapped some locks and spun the trolley around on its big rubber wheels, surprisingly smoothly on the gravel, and manoeuvred it up one stone step then another, over the lip of the threshold and in through our front door. We lined the tiled hall with our heads bowed as the trolley passed, as the remains of a murdered woman moved through our home, down the corridor and into the good room, where the armchairs had been pushed to the walls, the little nest of tables removed. A trestle table had been brought into the room and covered with a white damask cloth.

We followed the men into the room, crowded near the door to watch them snap the brakes on the trolley and unlock the grips on the casket. They moved around their cargo, checking, squatting then rising again, following one another's movements. I was reminded of airline stewards doing their safety checks at the doors of aeroplanes, running their unconscious hands over locks and handles, belts and buckles, reversing and swapping positions as in a dance, muttering their coded safety language. The masked men looked at one another and one murmured, and in a single smooth movement they lifted the casket onto the trestle table. They silently adjusted, straightened Sister Jenny's coffin, then stepped away.

Bonaventure and Simone stood at the end of the table, facing the last bodily remains of their friend. They stood with their backs to us, erect and calm. I had a vision of the two of them poised at the edge of a vast, flat stretch of water, like a sea or a lake, that they must now find a way to cross. I hoped one would reach for the other's hand, but they did not do that. At least, they did not do that in our presence, but then we left them in the room and closed the door. After that, who knows.

We waited silently in the hall with the funeral men, who stood – trained, respectful – with their hands clasped at their groins and feet firmly planted. Their eyes were downcast but now and then they glanced up, watching us from behind their masks. I watched us too, through their eyes. How strange we must seem, gathered here morosely in a hallway, no ritual to hide or protect or guide us. We heard a few sounds from inside the room. Low talking, some creaking of floorboards, and then a stretch of no sound at all. After a time the door opened and Simone told the men they must have a cup of tea, and gestured for them, for all of us, to follow her to the sitting room. She and Bonaventure led our little procession down the corridor.

I went to follow but then I stopped and went into the good room and stood alone with the bones. The casket is very plain, the wood unfinished and dry to the touch. I thought of that creature, the size of a large child, lying there dead in her box.

~

I don't know why I wrote 'creature'.

~

The car that delivered Helen Parry was a silver Audi with spatters of orange mud streaked along its doors. I watched from the good room window as her lean form levered itself out from the driver's seat, gripping the doorframe. She did not wear the veil, of course: as she emerged from the car I saw a navy sweatshirt, boyish blue jeans. Outlandish sunglasses, enormous on her face. She let the glasses drop then, and they swung from a cord around her neck as she turned to look directly at my window. At me.

I knew she could not have seen me here in the dark room because of the window's reflection, but still I felt my heart pitch in my chest. Physically, I mean, I felt it move with fear. Yet at the same time I knew she would not recognise me. It has been almost forty years since I spoke to her in the forest, and on that day she had looked through me, towards some larger purpose or experience than I could perceive.

Even back then, I told the bones inside their box, I was never visible to her.

~

In the sitting room Simone told the funeral men that nobody here would mind if they removed their masks. They glanced at each other, hesitant. Then the one called Pat peeled off his mask and put it in his pocket, and the others followed, inhaling quietly then, and rubbing their shaven faces.

Simone moved to speak with Helen Parry at the window, both of them inspecting the silver car parked in the driveway as they spoke.

The car belongs to the funeral people. Apparently she refused to be driven by one of the men, insisting on making the trip alone. She stopped along the way for some time, causing consternation for Pat, who thought she might have got lost. Pat had tried to phone her, he told Simone earlier, in a tone suggesting this was just one of the many trials of dealing with Helen Parry, but she hadn't answered.

But now she was here, holding a mug of tea at her chest and murmuring – yes, she told Simone, she was tired from the drive and the travels before that, and yes, she would like to go to her room now, please. Simone summoned Sissy and then, when Helen Parry had drained her cup, she turned from the window and gave us all not quite a smile, but a glance of acknowledgement, sweeping around the room, before following Sissy out.

Her glance had not slowed or stopped when it passed over me, and as she left the room there was a plunging sensation inside me, a spread of relief. But I don't think it was just me who felt it. A sense of expectation, a charged feeling, left the air at her departure, and some equilibrium now restored itself.

Just then a mouse darted along the wall near where the men sat drinking coffee. It sped out into the hallway from behind the sideboard. I don't think the men saw it but Josephine did, and so did I, and our eyes met. We were both thinking of the bones, I knew, because the mouse had gone in the direction of the good room.

The men were still sitting, eating pieces of the crumbly date slice I had made, when Richard Gittens walked in. Everybody looked everywhere, the men in a sudden outbreak of action: leaping up, nodding to each other, shaking hands, speaking more loudly to Richard than they had done to us, making their gruff noises of introduction and greeting. It was interesting to me, watching the men greet each other in this agitated way, as if it were essential they be seen in motion, as if it were necessary to assert themselves physically here in the female space of our sitting room. As though, in their drinking tea and eating cake, Richard had caught them doing something womanly. There was also unease, I suppose, to do with Richard's having seen them at all. Nobody but us is supposed to know about the arrival of the bones.

But for me, Richard brought great comfort into this moment with his steady presence.

The men put their masks back on and nodded in their sober, professional way at Simone before trooping into the hallway. Richard Gittens silently questioned me with his look – the hearse outside had alarmed him – and I could only shake my head quickly in reassurance, and that was message enough, because he took a piece of date slice from the plate and followed us all down the corridor to the front door, and he stood on the step with us, chewing, as two of the men got into their sleek black vehicle, started the motor and let its windows down. You could see their bodies relaxing as the car reversed. The younger one, called Kane, swung into the driver's seat of the silver car, rammed back the seat and simultaneously reached for the console. You could hear the cricket commentary floating up as the little convoy drove off down the gravel road.

Simone looked at Richard and then at me and said wearily, 'You'd better explain. But he can't tell anyone.' Then she turned down the hall towards her own bedroom.

'We have a visitor,' I told Richard, and gestured for him to follow me.

We stepped inside the good room and there was the casket on its table. Bonaventure was there, sitting beside it, crossing herself.

Richard looked appalled, then he too dabbed awkwardly at his chest. He stared at the casket and murmured, 'There's somebody *in* there?'

Bonaventure and I spoke at the same time. 'A nun,' I said, and she said, 'My *friend*.'

Richard did not know what to do. He said to Bonaventure that he was sorry, looking baffled, and then I led him out again. I explained – very briefly – about Sister Jenny. 'You can't tell anyone,' I said. I didn't add, *not even your wife*, but from other things he's told me I think it unlikely he would share with Annette many of the goings-on here at our abbey.

'And what about the other visitor?' Richard asked. He had seen Sissy and Helen Parry hauling her suitcase from the car.

'It's Helen Parry,' I said, and found that my hand was resting on his arm because I felt the kinship of our teenage years, that we were two classmates, and I wanted to protect the schoolboy in him from that time, from the casual brutality of things that went on.

But – unbelievably – Richard only asked, 'Who's Helen Parry?'

I waited for him to remember, but he just looked back at me with his grey eyes, innocent of any recall of Helen Parry and how she had been treated at our school. I felt a strange loneliness then, and a wave of fatigue broke over me. 'I'll tell you some other time,' I said, and Richard looked relieved, though I could tell he sensed something unusual was happening, and I think my touch on his arm alarmed him. It alarmed me too, afterwards, and I wondered if I had done it for his comfort or for my own.

He had only come to bring more traps, he told me. He had left a stack in the laundry for us. Bunnings was all sold out, but he had happened to walk in the door at Lucas's when a new order came in so he grabbed all he could get. 'They're putting a limit on how many you can buy at a time,' he said. I thanked him. He glanced up the corridor and then out at the space where the hearse and the Audi had been. Then he went outside and got into his truck.

I heard a mouse shivering along the skirting boards behind me, but when I turned around, it had gone.

WOKE WITH A sense that something uncanny has happened, something momentous. Then I remembered that a dead nun's bones are in the building and that Helen Parry brought them here, *is* here. I wanted to creep into the good room like a child, to stare at the box, and later I do. During the chant in the Middle Hour, stealing glances at the faces of the others, I thought, *You have, too.*

We have not seen Helen Parry this morning.

~

Richard told me some months ago that his wife had asked him to stop coming to our church.

Annette has come along with him once or twice since I have been here, but she has never spoken to any of us. She came one time I remember, a few years ago, and I watched her staring at us as we sang. Often, new visitors are concerned about following the prayers, shuffling through the booklets in a worried way. Or they close their eyes a lot, thinking of their private concerns. But Annette just stared and stared, watching our movements, and I knew she was storing up detail to report afterwards (to whom? Does she have friends, a sister?). I imagined her saying: *They kept bowing, sitting down, standing up, singing their weird songs about enemies and punishments.* Which is exactly what I said to my own friends, back then.

I returned my thoughts to the psalm and forgot about her. But later in the service I saw her face again and her expression had not changed. It was a kind of awed disgust that I saw there. Richard sat beside her, eyes down as usual, in his customary contemplative repose. I think he is usually working out calculations about stock, moving them between paddocks.

Afterwards, as I passed the church to collect the eggs, I saw Annette standing beside the small 'garden for lost children', inspecting it with her arms folded. I have never liked this garden. It isn't even a garden: it's a patch of crawling ivy on the southern side of the church, in permanent shade. In the middle of the patch there's a faded sign in the shape of an opened book, decorated with butterflies and babies and teddy bears and birds.

141

The 'pages' of the sign are designed as pillows, in a sickly pink colour. On one pillow, in blood-coloured, poorly lettered words: *A Garden of Remembrance for Little ones Whom parent's have lost through stillbirth, illness, accident or tragedy.* The opposite page says: *We hold them in our Hearts and in our Prayer.*

Parents whose children have died or vanished are able to 'plant' a little trinket or symbol there. Why choose this particular spot for this purpose? It is the dankest area in the whole abbey. The little memorial symbols are made of plastic or cheap plaster, and over the years they have faded to grey, as all plastic seems to do. The figurines are different, but unified by sentimentality and ugliness. Gnomes and fairies, mawkish statuettes of little girls and boys. A saint or Virgin Mary here and there. I watched Annette staring, and I imagined her disdain at this display. She, who owns the stylish homewares shop in town, with its beautiful, expensive things. (I have looked into its window, coveting the linen sheets, the ottomans woven in lush Afghan silks.) I was embarrassed for us, for the abandoned rubbish tip of a garden with its cheap symbols and its lack of attention, for it is a garden that says we most certainly do not hold in our hearts the dead babies and runaway daughters and ice-addicted schizophrenic sons. Instead, we pass them many times a day without a thought.

But then Annette squatted and I saw her pulling a strand of weed from between two of the little gnomes. She pocketed the weed and crouched there a little longer, appearing to read the children's names printed on the ugly grey sticks alongside their ghoulish manikins: the Elizabeths and Rhiannons and Aidans and Jessicas. Then Annette stood and walked into the sunshine to join Richard Gittens, who was leaning back against his ute, checking something on his phone.

When Richard told me what Annette had said, I asked him why he thought she didn't want him coming here. He chewed his lip, and then he said, 'She thinks there's something . . . sick about it. Something unnatural about the way you all live here.'

That was a few weeks ago, but he hasn't stopped coming. I have never asked him why he does come, and I can't say that I know.

~

I don't remember being told, but somehow I always knew that before I was born my mother had a baby boy who lived for just two days. I have always known that his name was Dominic, and that at the time of his birth my parents were separated by a flood. My mother had been unwell and her doctor had advised her to go to a Melbourne hospital early, before the due date, in case of complications. By the time the baby came, my father was unable to cross the floodwaters to reach her. My mother gave birth to the baby boy and two days later he died.

Mostly, if I asked her about this or other difficult times in her life, she would wave her hand and say, Oh, I don't remember. But when I was at university, I was given an assignment for some introductory feminist studies subject: to compile a personal history of a woman in my family. I wrote to my mother to ask about the birth of her first child and I was surprised to receive a long letter in reply. This was some time after my father had died, and perhaps that is why she allowed herself to write her letter. Or maybe it was the fact of not having to speak it aloud, or because the university assignment bestowed some greater authority on my request than if it had only been my own. In the letter she told me the details I knew, about the flood and the precarious pregnancy. But she also told me she remembered only two things of the time after the baby died. In the hospital after his death, my mother shared a ward with several other women, all nursing their healthy newborns. She told me she remembered lying in her hospital bed and thinking of the room at the end of the maternity wing, where she knew 'the illegit-imate babies' were lying motherless in their cribs, waiting to be adopted. She told me that every part of her wanted to walk down that hallway to the room, pick up one of those babies and bring it back to her bed with her.

The second thing she remembered was that on finally leaving the hospital – alone, to stay at a hostel for young Catholic women until the flood subsided enough for my father to be able to collect her – she was handed an envelope with her name on it. On the bus ride to the hostel, she opened the envelope and unfolded an invoice for the cost of burying her child.

My mother did not remark in the letter about her emotional state at the time; she simply set down what she remembered in plain language. But it was clear to me that between the quiet lines of that letter in her neat round blue handwriting lay a depthless grief and fury – and what is strange to me now is that in the remaining few years of my mother's life, she and I never spoke of it again. To my knowledge she never visited the place her baby was buried, or even tried to find out where it was.

But perhaps I'm wrong about that.

There were many things about my mother's life, her secret self, that remained hidden from me, and this was one of those things.

~

Annette may be right about the unnaturalness of our living here in the way we do.

But then, I reflect, there's probably something sick about the way most people live.

~

I do miss babies. Not that I wanted to be a mother – I have never wanted that – but I miss seeing babies, hearing their noises. Cradling a baby now and then at someone's party, or at a meeting. Mostly I miss catching a baby's eye on a bus, the way its gaze stays with you, serious and steady and curious, observing you from the little throne of its stroller. I did love that. I miss that, a lot. When I go into town I keep an eye out for babies, but I don't see them often.

~

I also miss the ocean.

A DREADFUL DISCOVERY: birds are eating the poisoned mice. We have found five dead magpies and a southern boobook. Dolores and I spent the morning digging a large hole and shovelling the dead mice into it from where they lay piled in the paddock. We wore latex gloves and surgical masks. A macabre job: the smell, the soft bodies tumbling by the shovel load. I closed my eyes as I pushed the shovel into the pile, lest I slice into the bodies or, worse, see something writhing. We could burn them in the old incinerator behind the tool shed, but decided against it, as we would have to clean it out too often – but I think the real reason is that none of us can face the imagery of burning bodies. The possibility of tiny unburnt skulls tumbling through the ashy haze. It's resolved: from now on no poison, only traps. And we will ask Richard Gittens about digging a bigger hole.

In the middle of this wordless, grisly work, for some reason a jaunty hymn we used to sing at school, 'God Loves a Cheerful Giver', came to me, and I thought how, oddly, it had always been associated in my mind with an advertising jingle for cordial, or maybe dog food. I started laughing, which made Dolores look at me, and as I began to explain, then sing it, her mystification made me laugh more. Soon she was laughing too and we couldn't stop. Mouse bodies raining from our shovels, and the two of us hooting hysterically, bent over our terrible work.

~

Once, while we shovelled, I looked up to see Helen Parry in the distance, marching off down the gravel road with her backpack. Most of her days are spent in the Nursery paddock, where she can get a signal, sitting cross-legged in the stubbly grass with her laptop and her phone, an old gardening hat of Simone's pulled down to shade her eyes. The latest travel restrictions mean her planned talks and meetings have been cancelled, so she's having to do them all on internet video calls. We hear her clear, strong voice floating across the paddocks, calling for action on this or that. Sometimes she shouts, overbearing, overruling.

To us, though, she barely speaks – unless it's to ask Sissy for something. An extension cord, a power board, a different chair for her desk, a small reading lamp, a specific brand of spiral-bound notebook. Cashews, and if there are lady finger bananas, because she prefers those. Also a particular kind of yoghurt, because the one we eat – the one I make daily – is too sour for her taste. I'm sent into town to buy these things. She makes her requests with a calm entitlement: 'as if she thinks the world owes her,' according to Sissy, who, infatuated at first, has grown snippy about her.

The rest of us try to stay out of her way. I have not told anyone about being at school with Helen Parry, about her mother, the housing commission flat, the schoolyard taunts, the attack in our sewing class. I even forget about it sometimes, but then I see her walking alone to her room with a plastic tub of soup in one hand and an electrical extension cord in the other and I know that what happened to her at home, at school, and what she learned from that time about fighting and survival, is still inside her. And the world does owe her, is what I think.

~

'Visitant': a guest or visitor like Helen Parry, or a supernatural being, an apparition, like a saint. Like a delivery of bones, like a plague.

Once, when I dragged the old yellow kayak out on the dam here, I saw something: a pale, translucent sort of smudge like a jellyfish, though less dense. Only when the thing flinched, as the oar parted the water, did I let the paddle sink to stillness and look more deeply. I saw – I thought I saw – a small face. I've looked for it every time since, when I've sat in that plastic kayak on the brown dam. A little face floating there like a delicate stain, a watermark on water. It's never come back. I miss it. I never felt in fear of that visitation.

A week ago, from the clothes line, I saw Helen Parry sitting in the yellow kayak in the centre of the dam, motionless, drifting. I will never ask her about the little face, of course.

~

I once heard on the radio a neurologist who specialised in treating epilepsy. He mentioned in passing that, in his experience, quite a lot of people with epilepsy were deeply religious. 'Quite a few nuns,' he said. The epileptic aura, the doctor explained, manifested in many ways: an unusual smell or taste, a feeling of a wave passing through the head. A sudden intensity of joy or fear, or bodily twitching, or visual disturbances of light. Hallucinations.

I thought of the tiny church I once visited in Provence, where Marc Chagall created a mosaic depicting the story of St Roseline, whose six-hundred-year-old desiccated corpse lay in a glass coffin in the same church. St Roseline, a young nun, was once so overcome with the adoration of God – mid table-setting duty – that she fell into an ecstatic religious swoon. She emerged from her reverie just in time for dinner, to discover that a band of angels had done her work for her. This is the subject of Chagall's sparkling work in the chapel, his childlike feathery angels floating above and beside a tea table.

All these centuries of paintings, all those saintly visions and miracles, all that religious feeling. Just neuroelectric misfire.

~

When I was living in Surry Hills and still working at the threatened species centre, not long after Alex had gone, I came home late one night, which was not unusual. But this time I entered my room and saw a coil of bedsheet twisted into a lump where I'd left it on waking that hot morning. A pillow was on the floor, and clothes and papers and notebooks and the iPad were massed on the unoccupied side of the bed. I was so tired, but the mess on my bed – the same congestion into which I had nightly crawled without noticing – was suddenly intolerable to me. I yanked at the sheet and the motion sent everything to the carpet. I lifted the sheet with two hands and it billowed slowly back down, and as it did I felt some otherworldly possibility open up inside myself. I picked up one of the pillows from the floor and placed it back on the bed, smoothed the sheet down to make a flat, empty expanse. I stood looking at the bed and breathing. It isn't something I ever told anyone – how could you say this? – but the lift and descent of that sheet, the air inside it, the peace when it settled, showed me what I wanted. I knew it in that moment, but it took years to find it.

~

The last thing I did on email before coming here for good was scroll and click. Threatened Species Rescue Centre: unsubscribe. Nature Conservation Council: unsubscribe. Rainforest Alliance: unsubscribe. Human Rights Watch: unsubscribe. Indigenous Literacy Foundation: unsubscribe. National Justice Project, Pay the Rent, Foodbank, Wilderness Society. Ethical Investments. Amnesty International, Red Cross, Climate Act Now, National Justice Project, Aboriginal Legal Service, Bob Brown Foundation. Extinction Rebellion: unsubscribe. Change.org: unsubscribe. Fred Hollows Foundation. Greenpeace, Green Living Australia, Action Network, BirdLife Australia, Daintree Buyback. Chuffed. org. GoFundMe. Helen Parry Legal Defence Fund. Unsubscribe.

~

There is something frightening about the bones being here, though nobody has said it. The door to the good room is locked and we are to check the lock whenever we enter and leave. We are not to touch the casket (hand sanitiser is available nonetheless, on the tea table inside the door). We are permitted to get the key from its hiding place on the sitting room mantelpiece and sit in there with Sister Jenny. To pray, or think.

There is also an unspoken fear that Helen Parry will one day leave her guest cabin and take up space here in our quarters. But for now she sits in the paddock with her phone at her ear and we try not to feel her watching us going into the church and out of it, into it and out of it.

Bonaventure spends long hours in the room with the bones, lighting a candle every time. You can tell when she's been in there because the scent of beeswax and struck match hangs in the corridors. I think she is mourning not only Sister Jenny but something in herself. Some secret, wrestling work is taking place, and I feel pity for her lonely labour.

FROM A DISTANCE, in town I saw Richard Gittens's wife Annette talking with another woman outside the supermarket. I knew it was her because she was so thin, her legs so long in the snug moleskins she wears. She has unusually narrow hips and a flat belly, neat as a box of chocolates. As I passed I caught her eye and was about to wave a greeting, but she simply shifted her gaze from me with one slow blink and went on speaking to her friend. I think she would be embarrassed to be greeted by anyone from our place. Perhaps especially by me.

Which suited me fine.

At the hardware, the last five rat traps they had went onto our account (still no working card machine). The traps are staggeringly, cartoonishly large. The wire is almost as thick as my little finger. I shivered, picking them up. After I signed for the traps, the kid said, 'Have a good day, Sister.' It happens once people know you live at the abbey, even if you don't wear the veil. Every time I hear it I'm reeled straight back into primary school, feel myself looking around for Sister Aloysius.

~

I have heard people who went to Catholic schools talk about the violence of nuns and brothers with a kind of survivor's pride for what they endured: rulers with embedded steel blades rapped over their piano-playing knuckles; a Christian brother who threw a boy against a gyprock wall so hard it broke a hole into the next classroom. But the only sadist at my primary school was a pretty, fashionable young teacher with a high curly ponytail, who wore miniskirts and long suede boots. I believe she truly hated children, and enjoyed inflicting humiliation and violence upon them.

~

After I saw Richard Gittens's wife in the street a rare feeling of freedom and peace settled on me about the life I am living here. Her countenance was full of discontent, even while she spoke to a woman I presume she would call a friend. I drove home in a state of gratitude and release, turning in at the gate and noticing every tree, every bend in the road, as if these things had been polished somehow in my absence, or as if a mirror, previously fogged, was now clear. Realised I had thought of this place as 'home'.

~

In a few weeks it will be Christmas, then the new year. It seems impossible that I have spent another whole year here, in this place, and yet to leave would be unthinkable.

CARMEL SAW ME scraping a few spots of blue mould off some bread and freaked out.

We had a brief spat over it – I suggested we think of the global hardship everywhere and not waste mostly good bread. She said *she* was only thinking of Simone's asthma, because inhaling mould was very bad for asthmatic patients. I said she wouldn't be inhaling it because I was cutting it out, and what about blue cheese in that case, but she had flounced out.

It's very lowering at times, to look back over the days here and consider my own words and actions.

A friend once told me in solemn tones that she'd known a girl at school who was so poor her mother used to splash water over stale bread and warm it in the oven to 'freshen' it.

I laughed. 'But my mother did that!' My friend blushed with mortification.

Later I wondered about my parents and money, but I knew we were not poor.

My mother had a series of oddball household practices, like scattering spent tea-leaves on the wooden floors when sweeping them. Somewhere she had come across the claim that damp tea-leaves would attract dust particles and prevent them being swept into the air. Sometimes she would be distracted or inter- rupted while sweeping, and our kitchen and living room floors would stay that way for a day or two, dotted here and there with little humps of dark, wet tea-leaves.

These habits of my mother's were not strange to me, and nor did they seem to come from any pinched or miserly impulse. It was more a kind of delight she took in finding new uses for things other people would discard. Even though I would cringe at the possibility of my schoolmates seeing her pull crumpled old plastic bags from her handbag in the supermarket, I still accepted these habits as part of my mother's nature. Now her practices would be viewed in a conservationist light, and I suppose that's what they were for her back then, too. But to me, in childhood, these strange ways of my mother's were just – her.

Carmel declined the bread-and-butter pudding that night, and I made very sure to show no reaction at all.

~

Once, when I was in high school, a note came home from St Ursula's warning parents about a sinister cult that had bought land outside of town. The Moonies, they were called, which was embarrassing, like a children's endearment: *horsies, doggies.* Enclosed was a petition for townspeople to sign to have the Moonies somehow banned or run out of town.

My mother and father were incensed. This had happened before, with the hippies who appeared briefly in the town supermarkets during a three-day Down to Earth Festival on a farm way out of town. These young people went shoeless, the men had long hair, and the women (people said) did not wear bras. There was a primitive vengefulness expressed towards them. There were rumours of obscene and animalistic ceremonies, and there was a general interest in the doings and relationships of these young people that my parents described as *prurient.* 'They have a right to buy their damned *groceries,*' I had heard my father say hotly to someone on the telephone.

Following the letter about the cult, my parents made an appointment for a meeting with my school principal. I heard this from other girls, not my parents themselves, though I knew they thought the letter was prejudiced. Nerida Broadhead told me they had accused the headmaster and the parish priest of religious bigotry, of persecution, that they had shouted, Why don't you mind your own business?

Many years later, my parents' benign opinion of the Moonies seemed to me naive. By that time the church had been criticised as 'predatory', and there were claims of exploitation and brain-washing. Harm was caused to the vulnerable, critics claimed. But I know what my mother would say now in reply about the Catholic Church, and she would be right.

'WE HAVE TO try to cure our faults by attention and not by will . . . Attention, taken to its highest degree, is the same thing as prayer. It presupposes faith and love. Absolutely unmixed attention is prayer. If we turn our mind towards the good, it is impossible that little by little the whole soul will not be attracted thereto in spite of itself.' Simone Weil.

Our Simone once took me to task over my 'sneering' about prayer. My notion of prayer was juvenile: forget this telephone line to God bullshit, she snapped, hot with impatience. It wasn't even about God, she said, which I thought must surely be blasphemous. Praying was a way to interrupt your own habitual thinking, she told me. It's admitting yourself into otherness, cracking open your prejudices. It's not chitchat; it's *hard labour.* She spoke as if all this were obvious. I longed to understand her. It feels always that I am on the edge of some comprehension here but never breaking through to the other side.

At night, just before sleep, is when I am closest to reaching it. In the morning, when the birds start, belief is as thin as the light.

A NEW YEAR.

The mice continue to worsen and Helen Parry is still here, like a trapped animal. She stalks the hallways now as well as the paddocks, almost always with earbuds dangling and a phone in her hand. There is more and more a feeling that she thinks we're goofing off here – unlike her, 'doing the work' in the real world. She's trying to organise a flight out of the country, but now it's almost as difficult to leave as to enter. Even from her cabin, we sometimes hear her forceful voice talking talking talking in the clear hot nights, and I remember her in the playground, striding up to people even as they turned their backs, waiting, forcing them to hear her.

She still hasn't remembered me and now I know she never will.

Still the permission for the burial has not come. Still Simone pursues the council, endlessly filling in the forms which then are lost and must be done again. Then someone else goes on leave. Then there's a whole new set of rules to be gone through, more forms.

It seems Helen Parry is working on a plan to go stay somewhere else, even if she can't leave the country. Nobody has the courage to say it aloud, but everyone wishes she *would* leave. And at the same time there's a growing air of offence that she's so desperate to get away from us.

~

We keep digging the pile of mice into the paddock – disgusting work – and the smell is intolerable. Richard Gittens is away and we have to wait for him to get back from holidays to help us find a better solution.

~

Coming back from town yesterday, car filled with groceries from the bulk-buy place, I stopped, as I sometimes do, to get out and stand looking down across the threadbare velvet-covered brown bones of this land. Stones and low yellow grasses and the delicate strings of barbed-wire fencing tracing long into the distance. Hot dry air zinging with grasshoppers. The sky a vast, white striated haze.

Afterwards, I heard an American professor say on the radio that his nation's racist history was a reckoning in waiting, and that this need for reckoning would never fade. He said it was like something from mythology, from a heroic quest, it was the thing that must be confronted for the kingdom to be well. The more you run from it, the more you run into it, he said.

Into my mind came old photographs of white Australian nuns and priests with rows of little Aboriginal girls and boys. The nuns' strong hands gripping small shoulders.

That night after supper I repeated the American's remarks to the others and waited for them to make the same connection I had. But Simone was concentrating on something in her thoughts and did not appear to hear me, and Sissy just looked at me with an expression of toleration. Dolores nodded in a vacant, acquiescent way at her knitting but said nothing, and the others had already gone to bed. I tried to will Simone and Dolores to look at me, to will Sissy into actually thinking about what I had said, but they would not.

Sometimes I want to stand up, overturn the tables, lock the doors, flick a match and burn this place to the ground with all of us in it.

The traitorous thought came that if Helen Parry were here right now, instead of in her cabin, she would have understood.

YESTERDAY I HEARD a shriek from Carmel in the kitchen. From its pitch, I knew it had to do with mice. There is something terrible in a quiet place about the sound of a woman's screams. It is worse than the sound itself; it gathers force, becomes an omen or a reminder of something horrible from the past.

I'm struck by how unremarkable it has become to empty traps every hour. The first dozen times, I took long minutes to set the traps, hovering in fear, afraid of having my fingers broken. The sound of every snapped trap caused a bodily jolt; I was revolted to the point of retching as I carried a trap at arm's length with eyes half-closed, and emptied it in horror out at the far fence. A couple of times, by accident, I flung the whole trap instead of only flicking it enough to loosen the creature and let it fall. But now I collect several traps at a time – often two

166

or even three mice taken in one trap – and wipe my fingers on my tunic after emptying and re-setting them. I have to remind myself to wash my hands afterwards. Half the time I forget to put a mask on until the stench hits me, but I can't be bothered going back so I just hold my breath as I near the trench.

So I called out from the dining room, 'Leave it, Carmel, I'll take care of them.'

But when I came to relieve her, she stood by the sink breathing heavily, her hands clamped over her face, closed against some ghastly vision. When I kneeled to pull out the traps beneath the stove I saw the reason: part of one of the dead mice had been violently gouged away. The steel bar lay across its soft body but in place of its head was a ragged, oily red stump. It's the mice, eating their brethren.

Nobody tells you this, about plagues.

They do tell you the mice will *eat anything*. Here, they have done away with the coiled plastic dishwasher pipes and the oven insulation, the electrical cord for the washing machine. All those tasks are now to be done by hand; there's no point replacing the parts until the plague is over. All the plastic food tubs have been thrown out; any cardboard, of course; and there are teeth marks in the plywood of the pantry shelves. And the piano.

But nobody told us that at a certain point the mice would begin to feed on their own dead. And what is most grotesque is this: every time I have found the cannibalised corpses, it is only the faces that are eaten away.

~

I remembered, emerging from sleep this morning, those first months after Alex went. We both knew it was my doing, though we never spoke of it that way, and for some time we left lying between us the possibility that I might eventually join him, that assumption we allowed people to hold in the world outside our marriage. But Alex had projects to run, and a fervour I could no longer even gesture towards.

One evening around that time I sat in a bar with a young woman who worked with me, and against my better judgement I confided my loss of hope. She didn't say much, but when she spoke her voice was filled with contempt: 'If you decide it's over, then it's over.' I looked across the table at her, and her beautiful young eyes said, *How dare you.* I saw the hurt go into her, and I saw how deep it went. She was barely twenty. I didn't go out with anyone from work again after that.

I read somewhere that Catholics think despair is the unfor-givable sin. I think they are right; it's malign, it bleeds and spreads. Once gone, I don't know that real hope or faith – are they the same? – can ever return.

In those first months I was so lonely that sometimes in the night I would get out of bed, take a wheat pack to the microwave and heat it, return to bed and hold it to my chest until I fell asleep. I think now it was a good instinct, a self-preserving instinct. But it makes me sad for the person I was at that time.

Another night, in that same flat in Surry Hills, just before sleep I felt a great certainty that death was coming for me that night. I was not sick, had no reason to believe this. I lay in fear, but also a kind of wonder, because it felt as if I had glimpsed an opening into some other state that waits for all of us. I've never had that feeling again, but I've known since that night that what I used to believe – that I was unafraid of death – is false.

~

I thought I saw Helen Parry watching me after we'd filed out of church after the Eucharist. But then she watches, sees, everybody.

~

I got my first job when I was fourteen, serving food to ski tourists in a motel restaurant owned by a Macedonian family. I was a terrible waitress. I forgot things people asked for – even when they asked repeatedly – and, once, my thumb dipped itself into a bowl of soup as I lowered it to the table. The man I was serving laughed and said, 'Jeez, I can't eat that, you've had your thumb in it.' But then he looked at my stricken face and said, 'Don't worry about it, love,' and I fled from his table.

I washed knives and forks in the kitchen one by one, until the mother of the Macedonian family nudged me aside, snatched up a dish brush with one hand and plunged a fistful of cutlery into the boiling soapy water with the other. She scrubbed at the bunch with savage efficiency before flinging the cutlery on the draining board: Like this! Quickly!

She once said, looking out of the restaurant kitchen window, 'Your mother is a great . . . *humanitarian*.' Which is how I came to understand she had employed me as some kind of favour to my mother, but I never learned what it was that she felt she owed.

~

My mother and father emigrated from Britain, each barely out of their teens, and they stepped onto the hard Australian ground stripped of everything but the new, the present moment, the suitcase handle in his grip, the wind whipping her hair across her face, the dank fishy smell of the quay, the *now*. They rarely spoke about their pasts. I used to like flipping through the album of their wedding photographs, because they were so beautiful. My mother's stylish dress with its peaked sleeves and enormous, bold collar rising from her slender shoulders; my father in a suit of tails and a waistcoat. I knew there had been nothing catastrophic, no war or poverty or earthquake or family disaster in either of their homes. They each just . . . got on a ship and left. So why did it always seem to me they had escaped death – actual or metaphorical – when they left their pasts behind?

THE COUNCIL STAFF are finally back from their holidays and Simone spends part of each day on the phone, patiently going through the whole story again, checking off the rules. Yes, the hectares; no, the proximity to drinking water. No: no closer to a copy of the death certificate.

Bonaventure still trudges into the good room daily, kneels there before the coffin, comes out again. At least four candles have burned down to stubs in there since the bones' arrival.

Despite her talk of leaving, Helen Parry is also still here. She and the bones are connected now in deeper ways. There is something about the presence of both here – the waiting, the rupture of it – preventing our little ecosystem from returning to its natural balance.

And Helen still does not eat supper or any meal with us, but now at seven o'clock, when we are at our private night prayers for Compline, she makes her way into our sitting room to watch the television news. Even from our different corners of the building we hear its noise. After the bulletin she switches off the television and returns to her cabin and her phone and her computer. The noise stops but the feeling doesn't, that she is leaving us with all the world's catastrophes, all the justice work undone, the poor unsupported, the natural creatures unprotected, rights unfought-for. She brings into our home, without apology, everything we so painstakingly left behind.

~

Dolores has had to stop making candles altogether because her raw wax has been eaten. Whole blocks of the paraffin, bags and bags of the flakes and pellets in the shed, that the silly girl didn't think to check until last week. What I don't understand is how eating all these things – electrical cables, wax, *concrete footings*, according to Richard Gittens – doesn't kill them. They survive, driven on by this relentless, ferocious appetite.

~

Now Richard and his family are home from their holiday at the beach (where Richard says it rained and rained but everyone was happy because *no mice*), he is coming to dig us a new hole. Or pit, as he called it. It will have to be deep, he says, and we'll need a lot of lime.

Most days we can see birds in the paddocks or the dried-out garden beds, industriously hunting: sparrow hawks, magpies, butcherbirds, ravens. Once they find a mouse they don't stop – stabbing, pecking, as the wounded thing hops and limps and flops about. Finally the bird holds down the convulsing creature with one claw, starts stripping and yanking at its guts, jerking as it gobbles them down.

~

Dreamed I had a beautiful pet: a type of small, sleek seal the size of a guinea pig. Its slick coat, and its soft black weight in my lap.

~

Late in the evening, around eleven, I heard a car coming down our driveway. Some minutes passed with the motor idling before a door opened and closed, and I could hear Helen's voice calling goodbye and laughing quietly into the night. Then the car circled around the old garden bed and drove off up the gravel road. It was Richard Gittens who brought her back last night. Or his wife, I suppose. But I don't think it's Annette whom Helen Parry is befriending.

I resolved to return to the labour of submission and obedience and attention and *work*, not rumination and gossip. Tomorrow, the chook shed.

PUTTING ON MY shoes this morning, I felt a soft mound just before the full weight of my left foot fell. I roared, stumbled, kicked the shoe across the room and the creature scrambled out. I had no time, and no choice but to put the shoe on again, but I walked with toes clenched on that foot, curving my arch all day, shuddering.

We spend hours now devising new systems, like luring them with peanut butter onto swing-top kitchen bins full of water, letting them fall and drown. It is morally appalling, this duty. A dense swell of horror lies beneath our discussions of how to do all this – looking for efficiencies, methods to be relied upon for swiftness and the least possible expense. We hear stories from further north in the state: mice in babies' nappies; women going to bed with pillows over their faces to stop the creatures crawling on them as they sleep. Children bitten in their hospital beds.

I've grown to hate them. Not just the plague, but the creatures themselves. Their stink, their rapaciousness and skittering feet. It's real hatred. I wait for it to pass, but I don't think it will.

At night is loudest, when the other sounds of the world are stilled. No birds, no psalm practice, no miscellaneous noises of an occupied abbey. Only mice feet overhead, pattering across the ceiling and inside the walls, a sound like dried leaves falling.

~

We are doing everything we can to avoid trapping in the bones' room. There would be something very wrong, we feel, about such violence near Sister Jenny's coffin. But soon we will have no choice. Every morning Bonaventure sets the wire-and-plastic traps outside the room, either side of the door, before she goes in there to sit. And within minutes the traps are heard snapping in the hallway.

~

'*And yet.* Those are my two favourite words, applicable to every situation, be it happy or bleak. The sun is rising? And yet it will set. A night of anguish? And yet it too, will pass.' Elie Wiesel.

~

The hammer blow when I learned, some years ago, that Carmel had left two children to come here. Two *high school-aged* children. Sissy told me this as we polished the hallway floor on our hands and knees one day. Sissy enjoyed that task: the symbolism of prostrating herself, rags in hand. She was breathless with admiration for Carmel, for the sacrifice she had made. But I felt myself rear upwards when she told me this, my body rejecting the entire notion of a parent voluntarily leaving her children. Sitting on my haunches, stunned, while Sissy shuffled backwards on her knees, scrub scrub scrub. I asked about the children: a sixteen-year-old girl, a fourteen-year-old boy. For a few moments I could not breathe for the hot plume of rage spreading through me.

About three months after that, two people came to visit Carmel: a thin young woman and man. I saw them getting out of a car in the drive, staring up at the windows. A little later – only an hour or so – they climbed back into their car and drove away again. I watched Carmel closely across the church later that day for any sign of turmoil or sadness, but saw none. If anything, she seemed more fervent, her voice stronger and more alive, her attention to the liturgy more avid. I looked up at the crucifix and the anger I felt towards Carmel poured through my veins.

~

Self-pity is the characteristic I have always most despised in others. Simone tells me that's because I have so much myself. We all hate the mirror, she says.

EVERY SO OFTEN, Richard Gittens's few sheep down in the Dungeon paddock put their heads up, take fright and go galloping off in one direction. I don't know why. Nor do I know why it is called Dungeon. Other paddock names here: Back Dungeon, Percy's, Top Percy's, the Scrub, Roped Down, Stone Yard, Nursery. I don't know who invented them or when, but I find these names enormously touching.

~

The feel of a poddy lamb's skinny back is like running your hand up the wrinkles in your sock. Their skins are larger than their bodies, until they fatten up. Last spring there were two, tottering up and down the wooden verandah where

Bonaventure made their little shelter beds once they were grown enough to stay outside, and they'd come charging to the laundry every time they heard the screen door squeal open. We had to mix the milk powder in the laundry and attach the teats very firmly before going outside. I learned that from experience – their mouths wrenching the teats from bottles so the milk emptied in one slosh to the boards, or their heads plunging deep into the bucket before the powder was out of the packet.

Bonaventure used to bring them in from the paddocks each season, wrapped in towels, and lay them by the fireside. One was called Violet, and she grew into a fat, healthy lamb who smelled beautiful. She would butt her little white face against your leg, and it was lovely to feel that urgent, needful touch. One day she went missing. We looked everywhere, calling and calling for her, but she was not found. We thought a feral dog must have crept into the yard and taken her, and I think we each secretly cried – and prayed – for her. But seven months later, Simone came inside with a grim expression and said, I found Violet. She'd got herself trapped behind a piece of corrugated iron leaned against a shed near the chickens, it seemed, and none of us had heard her bleating. What Simone found was drooping woollen skin and bones, and the little skull of Violet, pieces of flesh still attached.

We dug a deep hole on the other side of the chook shed and buried poor Violet in it. For a year afterwards the patch of ground was wild with green growth.

This past year there were no poddies. I don't know why, but the sheep were kept away, and nobody brought the orphans to us.

I ONCE FELT a kind of inhabiting presence in myself, during Lauds; something took up space inside me and spread along my shoulders and down my arms, into my fingertips. It was a sensation of heat, but not a pleasant one. It lasted around a minute, I think. It was the kind of heat I used to experience now and then during acupuncture: pleasant at first, but then intensifying into an almost burning sensation. It used to frighten me, but the acupuncturist was unsurprised, and seemed to think I was a bit of a baby for mentioning it.

In the chapel with that heat spreading through me, I thought with alarm, *This is either a ghost, or it is God.* And once this thought came to me the warmth dissolved. With my relief came a kind of shame at my cowardice. If I had not resisted it, if I had welcomed the heat – even the burning – what might have happened? Then I remember the epileptic aura, and any idea of ghostly possibility falls away.

~

One thing about my mother: I never knew her to laugh at anyone's belief, never ridicule it or challenge it in any way. No matter how outlandish or foolish she may privately have thought it, my mother was a person who respected the fact of belief in and of itself. It seems to me now that she could have opened her mind to any form of spirituality, really – except when it came to prejudice. When she saw bigotry or injustice, if she thought a person's belief would cause harm to others, she became incensed. People – at my school, at the church, elsewhere – disliked her then. Sometimes they closed ranks against her.

Some years after my father died, after my mother had folded herself up in grief for a time and then slowly emerged, dignified and altered, going about her life with the calm authority I've seen sometimes in people who have endured some great loss, she attended a yoga class for the first time in her life. I was staying with her at this time, though I was an adult by now and living in the city. She came home from the yoga school in a restless, agitated state. When I asked how the class had gone, she said that she didn't know, but it had made her start to *cry*. I thought she meant from some physical pain, but she said there had been no pain, just a terrible need to sob. So she had picked herself up from the floor, in the middle of the class, and left.

I was too young to know what I know now, and all I wanted in that moment was to protect my mother. I was angry on her behalf. There were people in the town, after my father died, whom I knew had been annoyed by the fact that they had not seen my mother cry. I never saw it either – not at the funeral, not before nor afterwards, but I knew this was natural for her, a deep need for privacy and stillness in her emotions, and I knew her grief was too great for mere tears. The mother of a schoolfriend of mine stopped me in the department store one day and asked me if my mother had cried yet. I wasn't confident enough to suggest that she mind her own business, and I replied vaguely that I wasn't sure, but I had not been present if she had. An irritability, even a kind of spite, came across the woman's face. She lifted her chin at me as she declared: 'She'll crack soon.' There was such relish in her voice I had to turn and walk away, and I never spoke to her again if I could avoid it.

When my mother came home from yoga in such distress I poured scorn on the teacher who had allowed this to happen, and I told my mother she never needed to go back again. She seemed relieved, but for the rest of that day her agitation remained.

Many years later I learned that expressions of intense emotion often take place when a person's thoracic spine is mobilised. It's to do with its relationship to the autonomic nervous system, which signals danger before our conscious minds perceive it – that system causing us to prickle with sweat, freeze, want to flee. The friend who told me this was a gifted physiotherapist. She told me she had seen patients break into uncontrollable sobbing – occasionally even hysterical laughter – when she had worked on this part of their spine. My friend (a scientist, after all) did not draw a relationship between the thoracic spine and its proximity to the heart. But she said patients had occasionally told her later of the enormous relief they had felt at opening up this seam of hitherto unexpressed grief or joy, and that something like peace settled upon them afterwards.

My mother never did go back to the yoga class. What did I know then? Nothing. What I know now is that my mother had been on the cusp of some new understanding of herself that day, something she both wanted and feared, and it was I who held her back from that discovery. Once more I wish I was able to be a wiser daughter to her when she was alive.

~

Do you have to believe in God to join a religious order?

Nobody has ever asked me, specifically, about belief.

And, anyway, I haven't ever joined. Not really.

DURING MASS THIS morning a low grinding noise began outside, and continued for the duration of the service. Afterwards I followed the sound to the middle of the paddock a way off beyond the back fence – Nursery – to find Richard Gittens sitting in an old red mini-excavator, digging a pit. He looked faintly silly, his big body perched in the little machine, working its levers and pedals. But the hole – the pit – was already large and deep, and as I approached he let fall another load of dark earth from the machine's toothed bucket to the pile of excavated soil. Richard saw me and turned off the motor. He sat in the machine and called to me across the big dark gash he had made in our paddock, explaining why he chose the spot – to do with water run-off (if it ever rains again). Then he pointed to a pile of white sacks nearby. This is lime, which we are to throw in after the bodies before we cover them with soil from the excavated heap each day. I nodded and left him to his work. It is necessary, but it looked violent, watching from a distance. That big blade, gouging and ripping its way into our earth.

Afterwards, over a cup of tea in our kitchen Richard told me that late last night, driving home from a dinner in town, he and Annette came across the strangest sight. Not far from their gate the surface of the road began to move. In this one stretch of bitumen there were so many mice crossing the road that he had to slow right down to understand what he was seeing. He and his wife sat, transfixed, floating across what seemed to be a wide river of silver water, flowing steadily beneath them.

~

This afternoon Josephine and I emptied the buckets and tubs of collected mice into a wheelbarrow by the back fence, bumped it across the paddock to the pit and tipped it in. Then we tore open a sack of lime, and shovelled a spread of it in white arcs over the bodies, followed by a thin layer of dirt from the heap. Afterwards we stood there looking down at the base of the pit, and felt we had entered a new and disturbing phase. Acceptance, perhaps, that the plague would not be ending anytime soon.

~

After that, the barrow fills quickly each day. From a distance, the shovels sticking out of the pile of dirt resemble crosses at the foot of a huge grave. Sometimes when I come back there's lime dust in my hair and on my tongue.

~

When I sit in the good room with the bones, I listen to the sound of mice inside the walls moving, moving, moving.

I have noticed that unless Bonaventure is in the room, I do not think of the bones as Sister Jenny. The word 'remains' is somehow insulting though; like leftovers. What are they, then? I think of them in their box: just bones, just a poor human animal, skinless and narrow and mud-covered. Evidence of unnatural sorrow, old hurt. Something that must be properly reburied for the kingdom to be well.

Twice now I have seen Helen Parry come out of this room and close the door, make her way up the hall and then outside, back to her cabin. Both times there has been something different about her; a slowness, a quietness. I wonder what she is telling the bones, and what they are saying back to her.

~

Richard Gittens told me some time ago that some Ngarigo people are fighting a private development to be built in a paddock not far from here, a place they believe to be ancient burial grounds. The site is next to documented Aboriginal graves, and a full archaeological study and subsurface testing were recommended by heritage and environmental experts. It has never been done. The developer says the heritage body has no authority to block the proposal. The build had been approved, he told a reporter. Why don't you write about something that's actually important? he asked her.

In our town when I was growing up, we were taught that no Aboriginal people had ever lived in our area; they'd only visited from the coast during the annual bogong moth season. (I hated those moths, bursting from behind our heavy school-room curtains in the spring mornings: enormous, furred. They would fall upon you in clumps, ten or twenty at a time, heavy and soft and dark, lazily flapping their sticky velvet wings against your skin.)

One of the men protesting the development says that at least a quarter of his fellow townspeople are Ngarigo descendants. We were always here, he said. We still are.

Almost thirty years ago, in another part of this region, flood-waters washed away a creek bed to expose the burial site of two people, a woman and a younger man, along with a toolkit and the most precious funerary goods yet discovered in the nation. The skeletons were dated at around seven thousand years old. The artefacts were taken into care by a cultural centre on the coast, but the remains were reburied near the flood site, in a ceremony conducted by a respected Elder.

It moved me to learn that when they were originally buried, the man and woman had been laid to rest side by side, their heads towards the water. I like to think of them still lying there, in the earth by the creek bed.

~

Any funeral I ever attended in a city finished in cremation. In our town there was no option but burial, so I never knew until adulthood that many see this as a particularly Catholic, particularly ghoulish practice. My friends who grew up in cities found it grossly morbid, to bury a body rather than burn it. I don't know why. They would shudder, speaking of worms and decay, appalled in some existential way. Perhaps it was the slowness of decomposition they found so horrifying. We don't want to think of our bodies gradually breaking down, our tissue leaking softly into earth. We want death done with, vanished like smoke into air.

~

Just when the misery of the mice, the drudgery and boredom of the days here feels intolerable, there is Dolores's pure, clear voice carrying across the courtyard as she practises alone in the church. I return to the peeling and coring of apples and find my work has become new, and beautiful.

~

A bad dream, of which I have only a dark weedy sense: an old friend, looming catastrophe, dread. The nights are still cool, even in January, and I woke with the thin blanket pulled up to my chin for protection, against the cold and from the dream. The sticky cobweb of it clung to me through Vigils, through showering, through breakfast.

I have only found one way to rinse off the bad feeling of such a dream. I made my way through the Nursery paddock – keeping as far from the mouse pit as I could, following the fence – and down to Dungeon, to the dam. I undressed on its gravelly edges and waded into the centre, where the water turns deeper and cooler. The surface was dark with reflection in the early morning, the sun beginning to rise in the clear sky. Cold water crept up my calves, thighs, over pubic bone to my hips, the gravelly sand turning to soft mud under my feet. I sank down and ducked my head beneath the surface and shot up again, the water's iciness forcing out that old dread-breath in a few gasps. When my breathing steadied, I lay and floated, the soft black water doing its absolving work.

Afterwards, dressing at the water's edge – pushing one wet foot into a shoe, then the other – I saw Helen Parry coming down through the Stone Yard paddock on the far side of the dam. We stood on opposite sides of the water and watched each other for a moment, and then she lifted an arm in greeting. I raised my hand in answer, and as she bent to remove her clothes I turned and made my way back up the hill, hair dripping cold water down my neck. At the gate I turned to see her in the centre of the dam, floating on her back, arms outstretched as mine had been.

A FARMER ON the other side of town has shot himself in the head. His neighbour found him in the paddock, shotgun on the ground beside him. The dead farmer had parked his Toyota on the road so people would know where to find his body. Under a windscreen wiper he'd left an A4 piece of paper on which he'd written in black texta: SUICIDE – CALL POLICE.

Our week's prayers, of course, are dedicated to his soul – and to his family, who will need them more. But the man's daughter, a nurse with the mobile BreastScreen service, told Richard Gittens she felt no anger towards her father, nor pity for herself or her sisters or mother. She did not need to forgive him, for there was nothing to forgive. She said severe depression had cursed her father his whole life, and that for him staying alive had been an unremitting torment. She was glad he had finally released himself from the agony of living, and released her mother from the sorrow and grind of trying to save him. And freed both of them from the knowledge that this day was always going to come. Richard said he believed every word the man's daughter said. She spoke with the austerity of truth, he told me. He used the words 'without guile', and then looked embarrassed at the formality of his own language. But in describing the daughter, Richard's bearing became formal too.

Then he lowered his voice and told me something else about the woman. She, the nurse, told him that every day since her father died she had visited his body in the morgue, to sit with him. Before he said this, Richard had been talking in the direction of the driveway gravel, but as he spoke these words about the morgue, he lifted his head and we stared at each other in fear. The woman had told him that each time she saw her father there, saw the cleaned bloodless mess of his face, she wept for all the decades he had been forced to endure his life, and for the way he had been forced to end it. The people at the morgue had been endlessly kind, she said.

~

From the day Helen Parry first arrived, Simone has weekly reminded her that of course she is welcome to eat with us, but she has always declined; she has work to do, and study,

195

and many calls to make. But last night Simone came into the dining room with a strange look on her face and then behind her entered Helen Parry. We scuttled around setting a place for her. I made sure to sit on the same side of the table as she did, at the far end, and I kept my head down during grace, which Simone said this time. Other than grace, no words were spoken during supper, and I don't know if that made Helen Parry's presence more or less unsettling. But during the meal I was reminded of that goanna stalking through the chicken yard to claim the eggs. It was something about the reach of her arm across the table and her grip on the serving spoon, and about her methodical chewing and swallowing, audible in the silence. It was the slow sureness of her movements, the absence of reticence, and the acceptance descending on all of us in the room of Helen Parry's natural right to dominate.

I wasn't the only one feeling uneasy. Bonaventure began fingering the old shingles scar on her forehead, between her eyebrows. I've noticed that whenever she's tense she rubs repeatedly at that spot between her eyes with her middle finger. I don't think she knows this.

Watching Helen Parry, the term *apex predator* came to me and then I was ashamed. Once supper was done and I was safely back in my room for Compline, I felt sorry for her. She must be lonely, to seek out our company. I did feel that sympathy for her. But that doesn't mean I want to see her at our table again.

~

Once, when I was around ten years old, there was an event in the town to teach us about world hunger. For one day we were to go without our usual dinner, and instead eat only a small bowl of rice – equivalent to the food a child in India would be eating for the entire day. The money that would ordinarily have been spent on dinner would be donated to a particular charity.

All of this was my mother's idea. The charity was an obscure English one, virtually unknown in Australia. She was the state's sole office bearer for the Phillips-Pelham Foundation, dedicated to relieving suffering in what we then called the Third World.

Occasionally a fat envelope would arrive at our house for my mother, stuffed with small items she was supposed to sell to raise money for the foundation. I don't know who she would have sold them to, for nobody had heard of the Phillips-Pelham Foundation, and the merchandise was not what you would call appealing, designed as it was to draw attention to the difference between Third World suffering and our own obscene wealth.

Once, the envelope contained a pile of small plastic-covered pocket diaries, and I stole one because I liked the miniature pencil that fitted into the diary's spine. I also liked it for a secret reason: the diary was illustrated on every fifth or sixth page with a black-and-white photograph of the people helped by the foundation. Mostly these were pictures of 'lepers'. I would take the diary into a corner and slowly turn its tiny pages, staring at pictures of children and adults with terrible deformities. Holes in their faces, mouths horribly shifted sideways, eyes missing. Hands with only tumours for fingers, or arms with no hands at all. I couldn't stop looking. I felt a compulsion that I could not explain, together with a sort of guilt: not that my life was so fortunate, or that the world allowed these people to suffer in this way, but that here I was, allowed to stare at them again and again, bringing the pages close to better see the swollen skin, the distorted faces. It was a second punishment, that they be made to stand there before a camera, apparently smiling, so I could spend these secret moments considering the despair of their lives.

There were about twenty people at the fundraising supper, mostly my mother's acquaintances and their children. I was a little older than most of them, and I stood in a corner of this desolate meeting room in the town, wishing we could go home. Eventually the rice was cooked, badly, and distributed in bowls. (Nobody in our town knew how to cook rice then except the few Vietnamese refugees my mother met with, and though she was sometimes invited to eat with them, she never asked them to teach her how to make fluffy rice.) The women stood in their flower-patterned trousers, talking earnestly, while we children stared, appalled, into our little dishes. When I received my own bowl I was swept with rage: why should I be forced into this? The soggy white plug sat on the dark ceramic surface, glistening, and the other children stared at me balefully and refused to eat theirs. But I was not allowed to refuse, and I gagged dramatically as I forced the sludge down. I hated my mother and I hated the Phillips-Pelham Foundation with its stupid name and its hopeless causes.

My mother carried on her small, pitiful fundraising activities for the foundation, sending them the earnings – fifty dollars here, thirty-two there – until she died.

SIMONE TOLD ME this morning that all three of the elderly sisters who used to be here – the ones who were collected in a little minibus and taken away to a Catholic nursing home in Sydney not long after I first arrived – have died over the past two years. The last, Sister Gerard Majella (Simone said her name with great fondness), went overnight. Bladder cancer.

I remembered these women shuffling into the church with their walkers, one in her electric wheelchair. Back then I thought that it would be a comfort, knowing you would grow old and die here in your home with your sisters around you. But that's not what happens, it turns out. You end up like everyone else, lying alone in a room, having your wet bed changed by gentle, underpaid strangers.

I suppose Simone feels she should be happy for them, for Hilda and Margaret and Gerard Majella, now they have *gone to live with Jesus in heaven*, but it didn't seem that way this morning. She seemed confused, as if she had not anticipated those old women would leave this earth. Perhaps there is new understanding that the generation before her, her group of elders, has now vanished. Knowing that she has taken their place.

~

Fourteen eggs today: a record. I think the chickens are getting fat on the mice.

When I first landed here, I heard from my cabin the faint trills and cheepings of the newborn chicks that had hatched in the henhouse. I came to know some of those same young hens through their entire lives, feeding them curl grubs from the garden, dusting them with diatomaceous earth for ticks, rubbing Vaseline on their combs in the coldest months. I collect the eggs, still warm from their bodies, and in time I have buried some of them, after an illness or the catastrophe of a fox attack.

I never had to learn to kill a chicken. I saw Bonaventure do it once, expertly scooping up the bird, holding it close to her breast while she stroked its back and said a prayer. Then she laid a shovel on the ground and raised one end of it by stepping on the blade, at the same time laying the bird, now so calm it seemed tranquillised, on the dirt. She nudged its head beneath the shaft of the handle, then lowered the handle to gently trap the creature's neck, still stroking it. Then in one swift movement she stepped down on each end of the handle and yanked up the creature by its feet, instantly breaking its neck. I heard the pop. The flapping continued for around a minute and she prayed again over the creature, smoothing its feathers and murmuring loving words. She said the flapping was just electrical impulses through the muscles, that the chicken had lost consciousness instantly and felt no pain.

I knew she hated to do it. I turned away so she couldn't see my distress. It was up to me to pluck the bird, which I did with relief at not having to kill it, dunking the lifeless creature several times in the water boiled on the gas burner out on the back flagstones.

But around the time the old sisters were taken away, we decided to kill no more chickens. I don't know if there was a connection between those things – the death of the birds and the collection of the old women in their wheelchairs and walkers, taken to a place they would 'be more comfortable' – but soon after that day Bonaventure announced she didn't want to do it anymore, that it was needless death, and Simone and the rest of us agreed.

Once or twice a year Richard Gittens turns up with two large chiller bins on the back of his ute, each full of roughly butchered cuts of frozen meat, and we accept his gift gratefully, loading the bags of mutton chops and legs and neck bones into the chest freezer. We will not refuse a gift of food, but most of the time we go without meat in preference to ending an animal's life.

~

This morning after Vigils I went back to the church alone for a while. There was a flapping sound above me, and I saw that a bird, a kind of pigeon, had got in through one of the half-opened windows. It flapped from one side of the empty space to the other, and so I went to each of the doors and opened them wide to let it out. The light poured in. I sat, watching the pigeon as it flew and then landed, flapped and landed. Eventually it settled on the floor near the open door, drew back its head, and walked out into the sunshine.

I described the bird to Richard Gittens later in the day and he told me it was called a peaceful dove.

IF A BIG rain comes it will rid us of the mice, we're told. This is what has happened in the past, up north. But nothing about this plague resembles what has happened before, we are also told. Simone asks that each of us pray, with special focus, for God to take care of the plague. I think it's strange she imagines we have been praying for anything else this whole time. When you hear the creatures scuffling around your bed at night, it's fairly persuasive.

This morning one sat watching me from the top of the tiled wall as I showered. I shouted and it didn't move, even when I waggled the shampoo bottle at it. I had been about to wash my hair but its unafraid staring gave me the creeps. Even the idea of raising my arms and exposing my chest was frightening. Ridiculous. But their power is beyond physical now;

it's become mystical. It's worst in the church, watching them shooting from their hiding places as soon as the organ starts up. I know Josephine makes her way into the church very early before each of the hours, to dispose of what she finds on the dreadful sticky mats. We're all appalled by the sticky traps, but we can't afford to lose the organ. I try hard not to see the stamps of bright yellow in the barrow.

Everywhere, the smell is getting worse. The only place they have not appeared, most strangely, is the good room, though they are in the walls, and scurry along the outside windowsills.

We pray for rain. Even Richard Gittens prays, I think. He comes and kneels and closes his eyes and clasps his hands, where he used to just sit and stare.

~

I once went to a wedding where the bride's brother brought along his difficult girlfriend, and things did not go well. Her name was Cleo. My boyfriend was the bride's other brother. The wedding was beautifully planned. There was a service in a picturesque village chapel, and a reception in the town's fanciest restaurant, which was not very fancy but the best that could be had. I was keen to be helpful; I looped floral things over the ends of the pews, and set out name cards on tables. Cleo was nowhere to be seen during the wedding preparations, but that was fine with everybody because Cleo had a propensity to challenge and disagree, always with a wide, serene smile on her face. She was a very pretty girl, with thick dark wavy hair down to her waist. I think she may have had a tattoo somewhere discreet – a frangipani, or a small blue butterfly. Cleo wore flowers in her hair and bright flowing skirts, when girls like me wore jeans and bulky, dull-coloured sweaters. It only occurred to me in late adulthood, seeing young women in the street, on the beach or in restaurants, how strange it had been that I covered my young body so thoroughly and constantly back then. But Cleo had a lovely body and saw no reason to hide it.

Cleo's main crime was to be a vegetarian, a tremendous source of affront for the mother in this family. Vegetarians, in those years in our kind of country town, were regarded with suspicion and annoyance. They were trying to get attention, was the general idea. Cleo didn't care what people thought, and often brought her own food to social occasions. Carrot sticks and cubes of cheese, or just an apple, while other people sawed into slabs of overcooked steak.

The wedding restaurant did not cater for vegetarians. This was announced to Cleo's boyfriend, the brother of the bride, as a warning. She could eat around the meat. Everybody saw this as perfectly reasonable. It was the bride's day. Surely even Cleo could see that. And Cleo did, it seemed. She greeted the bride and groom sweetly, she dressed sweetly herself in a pale, modest gown with sleeves and wore no make-up, her pretty hair tied up in a loose bun. She wore elegant sandals, carried a small beaded drawstring bag and did not create a fuss in any way.

When the waiters came around with their plates of chicken or beef, Cleo smiled charmingly and waved the dishes away. The brothers and I looked on as she took a plastic-wrapped white-bread sandwich and put it between her knife and fork at the table. While everyone took up their knives and started ripping into their congealed meat, Cleo unwrapped a peanut butter sandwich and ate it daintily, smiling across the table at my boyfriend, sipping from the champagne we were supposed to leave for the toasts.

The family's mother was at the bridal table, but I could see her staring down the long white corridor of our table for twenty, enraged. I don't remember the rest – there was dancing and speeches and we were all rather drunk as, late in the evening, after the bride and groom left and everyone had gone home, we trawled the tables for forgotten belongings, making sure cards were attached to gifts and saving the floral centrepieces for our mothers and their friends. Cleo sailed about, picking up something here and there, but mainly working at her given vocation, which was to absorb the family's rage. Everybody hated her for the scene with the peanut butter sandwich, for making herself the focus of even *this* occasion. In fact, I don't know that more than three or four people noticed the sandwich or cared, but that was immaterial. She had done it deliberately – as she committed all her offences – to create a disturbance. Even her boyfriend, my boyfriend's brother, did not defend her. He merely ignored her as he – enduring the secondary punishment, of silence from their mother – went about his chores.

I was staggered by how little Cleo seemed to mind the family's hatred. She smiled and chatted in her pleasant way. In the taxi we four shared to get home, the air thickened with my boyfriend's fury at her and mine too, out of loyalty and something less identifiable. I couldn't wait to get out of the car. As the taxi sailed down the town's empty roads with their lonely streetlights, Cleo said mildly, 'It's a full moon. Everyone goes crazy on a full moon.'

~

The mother of that family was the second mother. The first mother – the mother of my boyfriend and his brother, though not of their sister the bride – had gone missing on a family trip across the Nullarbor Plain when the boys were small. The family had been camping on the flat desert plain. In the far distance you could hear the ocean; it was one or two kilometres away, crashing at the bottom of the massive cliff, where the land fell into the sea. They had camped in a large canvas tent, of the kind many people had back then. They slept on folding wooden beds with canvas slings. In the morning, their mother had disappeared.

Search parties, police, helicopters. Trackers crossing the desert with dogs. Their father was suspected, then not. Their mother was never found. An inquest determined she had probably walked to the edge of the earth and, deliberately or accidentally, fallen off. The cliffs around that area are hundreds of metres high.

When some years later the father remarried a woman with a quiet older daughter and a marital tragedy of her own (her husband, killed, had been a long-haul truck driver), the boys were still in primary school. After my boyfriend told me the facts about his mother he never spoke to me of the loss again, except to say that when his father announced the remarriage he, the younger child, had cried and begged for this not to happen. He dreamed nightly that his mother would come back to find herself replaced, and leave again.

He had no memory of the long drive home from the Nullarbor – it took five or six days, he thought – to our town. He thought his brother, who was seven, sat in the front seat for the journey.

~

Not far from the edge of town there's a dam with a wire fence running through the middle of it and out the other side. Perhaps it's more accurate to say the dam has formed itself across the fence line. I look out for it every time I pass; there is something forlorn about the thin fence posts pushed sideways by the water's weight, or perhaps some muddy weed, before they straighten again and continue doggedly up the hill on the other side of the dam.

I used to think there was a 'before' and 'after' most things that happen to a person; that a fence of time and space could separate even quite catastrophic experience from the ordinary whole of life. But now I know that with a great devastation of some kind, there is no before or after. Even when the commotion of crisis has settled, it's still there, like that dam water, insisting, seeping, across the past and the future.

~

I have discovered more gruesome tales of the saints in the cloth-bound book. St Margaret Clitherow, pressed to death on her back over a sharp stone by a door 'weighted down with eight hundred pounds'. 'Her death took fifteen minutes,' says the book. There is St Philomena, the virgin martyr and patron saint of babies, who at thirteen years old was 'desired' by the Emperor Diocletian. On refusing him, the girl was beaten, imprisoned, tied to a pillar and beaten again. Tied to an anchor and flung in a river. Pierced with arrows. Protected by angels who rescued her from each attempt on her life. The angels eventually failed, it seems – she was decapitated. Not a lot of rape is detailed in *Stories of the Saints*, though you have to wonder. You'd think it would have been a routine part of the mix, along with the eye-gouging and drowning and the rest. Perhaps that's one of the reasons Maria Goretti had been so compelling to us – the acknowledgement of what was left out everywhere else. *Sister,* if Maria had lain down and shut her eyes and endured the sinning but not the stabbing, would she still be a saint? *Sister,* if Maria had stabbed Alessandro to death with his own awl would she still be a saint? *Sister,* if Maria's mother had not forgiven Alessandro, if instead she had spat in his face and cursed his name, scratched his face, kicked his balls, shot him, taken to his cock with her own carving knife, would Maria still be a saint?

DURING MY RUN this morning I heard footsteps behind me on the gravel, and soon Helen Parry was by my side, keeping pace. Not difficult to do: I'm a slow runner, though I like to remember the technique I was once told, the arms swinging loosely from the shoulders, each hand drawing back as if to take something from a side pocket. Occasionally when I run, I feel it as a form of flight. But not often. And not today with Helen Parry alongside me, when I felt sweatier and breathed more heavily than usual.

She greeted me with a nod, and ran alongside me. She wore a pair of loose old running shorts, and a thick sports bra under a greying Greenpeace t-shirt. The t-shirt neck was stretched, fell to one side so you could see the racerback bra strap. Old black

Nikes, white ankle socks also turning grey with age. A navy blue baseball cap, printed with some school crest or other.

We ran together like that, our strides matching, for a short distance. I began to slow my pace as I neared the gate, the point at which I always turn around and run back. Helen exhaled a half-smile and nod in my direction but did not slow down as I did. She kept going, taking the cattle grid in a single long stride – risky; the bars are widely spaced and slippery – and then went through the gate. She turned right, taking the side road in the direction of the Gittenses' place. I stood catching my breath at the gate, watching her run down the empty road in her ungainly style. A little hunched, shoulders too high, but not breaking her stride. I watched until she went over the small rise and I couldn't see her anymore.

Afterwards, as I peeled off my t-shirt and socks in my room, my sweat smelled strong to me and I wondered if Helen Parry had noticed it. Probably she had, though she didn't show any sign of this.

Much later, on my way back from the Middle Hour, I passed her in the yard as she returned. I asked her how her run was, and she said it had been fine. She didn't look at me as she spoke, finding something in the trees to focus on. She had run down to the Gittens place, and Richard Gittens's wife had driven past her on the road and invited her to their house for a cold drink or a cup of tea, and she had accepted. I felt something disquieting roll through me when she said this. I don't know why. She said that Annette was an interesting woman, but 'quite uptight'. She wiped her arm across her forehead and as she did this the lift of her arm showed the full curve of her breast beneath her t-shirt. After the cup of tea she had run back. I wanted to know if Richard Gittens had been there but something stopped me from asking. Then Helen asked if anyone from town had phoned for her and I said I didn't think so, and she smoothed a hand over her throat and pulled her t-shirt away from her chest. She said she needed a cool shower and turned towards her cabin.

Later I remembered Virginia Woolf saying of Katherine Mansfield – the only writer of whom Woolf was ever jealous, she said – that when Mansfield came to visit her 'she stank like a civet cat'.

~

For a brief period in the 1970s, some of the Catholics in our town were swept up in a new craze for organising worship sessions in their own homes, in the hope that ecstatic spiritual events would unfold. My mother changed the subject at any mention of these people – 'the Charismatics' – whose claims included speaking in tongues and religious intoxication to the point of fainting, bodily overcome by the Holy Spirit itself.

In their disapproval my parents found themselves strange bedfellows with the local priest, who quietly discouraged Charismatic theatrics and urged his parishioners to stick to mass for more traditional, and more orderly, forms of prayer. Looking back, I think my parents' disdain had as much to do with what they perceived as American chicanery as their general scepticism about physical manifestations of the Holy Spirit. I understood these meetings to be run by people who thought themselves somehow special or gifted, or who sought out drama (a great crime).

I think now my mother must also have sensed a kind of sexual undertone to descriptions of these gatherings – there was a furtiveness, a breathlessness and urgency in the reports of the wild abandon of self, the rumoured loss of all control. Perhaps she was thinking of one of the teachers at my school and her husband, who were rumoured to spend their weekends 'wife-swapping' with the next-door neighbours.

One of the homes at which the Charismatic meetings were held belonged to my friend Kelly and her parents. Although I often attended Sunday mass with this family, I was forbidden from attending these meetings. Nevertheless, in the late afternoon of one autumn weekend, Kelly and I helped her mother set out little cut-glass bowls of peanuts and French onion dip with Jatz crackers for a gathering that evening. Mrs Fuller spoke of 'signs and wonders' and 'Charismatic gifts', the extraordinary powers that could descend on a person who, after a period of intense prayer, was filled with the Holy Spirit.

All of this was riveting to me.

People began arriving at the Fullers' door, alone or in couples, one or two carrying a bottle of wine. One woman, who arrived early, was more sophisticated than most women in our town. Her bold jewellery and hair, her declarative way of speaking, manifested the authority bestowed by being from somewhere (almost anywhere) else. Her name was Jackie, and she was from Canberra. She had driven here to lead the meeting with her husband, Rob, a tall, fit-looking man who smiled generously and told everyone several times that he was from Minnesota, which drew exclamations.

Mrs Fuller's friends were another middle-aged couple and their sixteen-year-old daughter, inscrutable with harsh make-up and silence, and three droopy-looking young men who were generally seen hanging around the church doing small tasks for the priest: handing out hymn booklets, mowing the lawns. When I grew up it seemed clear to me that the church, and gentle Father Fitzroy in particular, must have offered the only place where a meek young gay man might feel protected, even welcomed. There was also the town's Little Theatre, where all kinds of artistic cavorting was supposed to go on, but these boys were far too shy for that.

After a time, the front door was closed, Kelly's mother lit candles all around the living room, and the overhead lights were turned off. Glasses and coffee cups were set down as Rob pressed play on a little cassette player. Jackie and Rob produced two tambourines, swaying along with a jangly pop hymn, eyes closed, crying out one melodious line over and over: *Come, Holy Spirit*. On television I had seen Hari Krishnas dancing and singing in the streets – in cities, nowhere near our town – and those images of blissed-out, shaven-headed believers came back to me as Mrs Fuller now raised her arms, her eyes tightly closed, and soon everyone was swaying and singing along in their hesitant, small-town voices in the candlelit dark.

When the hymn was finished, ending with a long shimmer of tambourines, Jackie began instructing us in a strong, clear voice, eyes still closed, hands high in the air. We were to do three things, she said. First, we were to pray with *expectant faith*. This meant to fully believe that our prayer would bring definite results; that God would listen and answer this prayer without question. Second, we must keep singing 'Come, Holy Spirit'. We must not stop, for this was calling forth the Charisms. And third, if we happened to hear unfamiliar words in our heads, this was the Gift of Tongues, a holy language coming directly from God, and we must speak the words aloud.

The singing began again, and I opened my eyes a fraction to look around at the faces of Mrs Fuller, Mr Fuller and their friends – smiling, singing, swaying along. *Come, Holy Spirit.* Mr Fuller's expression was of mild forbearance. Once Rob and Jackie took up the hymn again in their full, carrying voices, Mr Fuller opened his eyes and silently darted about the room between the swaying worshippers, collecting up coffee cups and ashtrays, then slipping out to the kitchen. The visiting teenage daughter swayed stiffly but did not sing, while her parents obediently shifted their weight from one foot to the other and back, valiantly repeating the words in their thin voices. But it was the young men who were truly affected. In the darkness, with this chaste encouragement, they began to unfurl. Their bodies moved gracefully, a natural limberness descending into their hips and their chests. Their hands reached high in the air, delicate underwater fronds, and they sang softly, full of yearning.

Then a quiet gasp was heard and I saw that Mrs Fuller had begun to tremble, breathing heavily. Jackie moved to her and nodded, smiling widely, then closed her eyes again, singing on and on. Everyone else stepped back a little from Mrs Fuller and then we all stopped singing because she had thrown back her head and opened her mouth to emit a long string of strange noises, a made-up African-sounding language, her 'accent' changing every few phrases. Mrs Fuller's eyes were tightly shut as she swayed and called, in the grip of something animal, some urgent force. In the candlelight her throat glowed with a fine perspiration and her voice took on an anguished tone.

Jackie began calling out over Mrs Fuller's voice, translating her speech into holy praise and pleas. And now Mrs Fuller was beginning to cry and wail in her new language (I noticed she began to repeat some of the first 'words'), and opened her eyes briefly before letting herself fall into Rob's waiting arms. With surprising smoothness he steered her body to the sofa, draping her across it. It was an agile operation that made me think they had done this before. Mrs Fuller lay in an ecstatic swoon, arms above her head, chest heaving, as the others sang on triumphantly. Mr Fuller had come out of the kitchen and stood watching all of this from the doorway.

Afterwards, when everyone had gone home and Kelly and I lay in her room in the dark, I wondered. I found it impossible to believe Mrs Fuller had been filled with the Holy Spirit, but still I felt a kind of reverence for what had gone on. The young men and their yearning, the thrusting of the self into some new vulnerability, the willingness to be opened up – all of this seemed beautiful to me.

At home the next day I told my mother we had eaten tuna mornay for dinner and watched *This is Your Life* on television. I believe she knew I wasn't telling the truth, but she asked no more about it.

~

I dream: Helen Parry dancing, her head on fire. The flame is long and thick, covering her whole head from the neck up. She shrieks and tosses her head in circles, the flame swirling out like hair. The shriek isn't pain or fear but exhilaration. A sound of power, just on the edge of terror. Sweat pours off her along with the flame. There is something potent and ceremonial in her dance, in the fire and the sweat. It is a kind of holy rite.

HELEN PARRY WAS not at supper this evening, as she has been for the past several weeks. I assumed she had taken her meal (cauliflower soup, not my best work; strangely watery) to her room, but Carmel said no, she didn't know where she was. At the Gittenses, I supposed.

Everyone is sick of her. Bonaventure seems to be the most affected; cowed in a way I find heartbreaking. I watch her waiting to see where Helen Parry will sit, and carefully choosing the other end of the table. I watch her arranging her face if Helen speaks, so as not to show her real feelings; her ignorance, or uninterest or fear of judgement. But it's as if her distress is chemical, and Helen can smell it, for she seeks Bonaventure out with her minor, annoying requests. She appears to see her as some kind of servant. And Bonaventure serves. I can't stand it.

So tonight, with no Helen Parry at the table, there was a harmony in the air that we have not felt for a long time. Also – it is too early to tell, we do not dare hope, but – there seem to be fewer mice these past few days. Somebody said it but then we knew not to tempt fate; we just closed our eyes and said grace together.

~

In the good room today Bonaventure revealed what's beneath her feelings about the bones: she and Jenny had a terrible, wounding fight here at the abbey before Jenny left. Bon couldn't bear Jenny's insistence on the immorality of staying: accusations were made, they told each other vicious truths, Jenny left and Bonaventure grieved. No apologies were ever made nor forgivenesses offered, and with news of Jenny's disappearance came Bonaventure's eternal anguish. This is the cause of her penance, her vigil before Jenny's coffin.

I sat with her as she told me this, and after she stopped speaking I held her soft dry hand and we watched the coffin together for a while. We all make saints of the dead, I said. It's the only way we can bear it. There was a moment then, while Bonaventure decided whether to tell me the truth – I could feel her weighing it up – and then she told me I was mistaken. Jenny was, is, no saint, she said. It is not that she wishes she had apologised, sought Jenny's absolution. It's the opposite. Jenny has gone, and Bonaventure is left with the great mess and injustice of what happened, and her own anger refuses to subside. 'I'm not praying for her forgiveness,' she said. 'I'm trying to find a shred of it in myself.'

She told me that, and I could see the cold hard weight of it in her, and I believed her when she said she thought it would never leave. She got back down on her knees and I left her there, head bowed, one palm resting on the cross of the casket's wooden lid.

IF YOU DON'T live the life you are born for, it makes you ill. That's what Helen Parry told us this morning, dispensing wisdom. Helen's Buddhist friends in Thailand say it is a matter of your dharma, she said. You must live according to your own dharma, even if you could be very successful at living someone else's. If you don't live your rightful dharma, then you will cause grave spiritual injury to yourself.

I remembered an artist I knew in my twenties. He said an unfinished painting was a form of malignance. He said an artist must complete their work, good or bad, lest it make them sick.

After Helen Parry made her condescending remark at the breakfast table, she didn't appear to hear Bonaventure respond very quietly, 'I was born for *this* life,' and I understood that this is not just a fight with Helen, but with Sister Jenny.

What I could not tolerate was the 'falling in love with Jesus' talk that I knew would come next, and it did. I find it nauseating; surely this life should be composed of something more sober than that. Something austere, and momentous, and powerful. Close attention, hard thinking. A wrestling, to subdue . . . what? Ego. The self. Hatred. Pride. But no, instead we have Sissy, and also Carmel, simpering that they are here *because I fell in love with Jesus and want to live with him in heaven.* As if they're talking about some teen idol crush. I have learned not to roll my eyes but there are times it is nearly impossible. Right at that moment, forcing myself to stay at the table, I was surprised to find myself meeting Helen Parry's glance, and more surprised still that both she and I held each other's gaze. Then she gave a tiny movement of her head in microscopic mimicry of Sissy's and Carmel's simpering, and I had to turn away not to laugh, in the process most completely failing to subdue my ego, the self, pride.

Sissy is no fool, though. She saw, and she faced Helen Parry at the table and asked her in a sweet, dangerous voice: 'Why *did* you come here, do you think, Helen?'

Her question was a shocking one, I think to all of us. Helen left a pause before replying, smiling, 'To bring Sister Jenny home, obviously.'

She looked around the table, and then she and Sissy met

each other in the moment of silence that followed, and Helen considered the question inside this silence before, finally, she showed herself to us. 'And to see my mother,' she said, 'before she dies.'

226

PART III

AUTUMN IS HERE. The poplars and willows along the creeks have turned their creamy yellow, and it is Ash Wednesday, and we remember that we are dust.

Recollection: a priest's thumb smudging the sign of a cross on your forehead; sweet-smelling ash-dust falling on your closed eyelashes.

Filling the birdbath after Vigils this morning, I realised that the muffled flapping of the cockatoos' wings as they swoop down to the bath resembles the sound of the mice scuttling in the night. The mouse plague is infecting everything now: all sense of smell, of course, but even sound, even memory.

As I wound the hose back around its wheel I remembered the boy from our town who grew up to shoot his parents dead. There were a lot of rifles around at that time. My own father even had one, tucked away in a box on a high shelf, though I never knew him to use it. I don't recall how I discovered it was there, or why he would need such a thing. There was a tale of his shooting a snake once, in his teaching days in a bush school. The children crowded behind him while he took aim at the sleeping brown snake. After it was killed it made a long hissing noise, which he found strange. Then the schoolchildren began shrieking in delight: he'd shot his motorbike tyre, and the snake slowly slithered away. The rifle in our cupboard took on the affectionate patina of this story. What I remember of the gun is the warmth of the brown wooden butt, glossy, inviting. When did I see this? I seem to recall a reverent opening of the box, green felt lining (like that of the box for the little cut-glass offertory jugs), a slow inspection and then replacement of each part of the weapon. But this may not be a memory at all, it could be something from television or a book. At some point before I reached adulthood the rifle in our cupboard disappeared, without anything being said.

The family of the boy I remember owned the Coronation Cafe in the main street. The mother and father lived in the flat upstairs from the cafe, and the boy lived in a caravan in the backyard. There was an older brother, but I don't know where he was at the time this happened, whether he too lived with the family or whether he had moved away. One weekday evening an hour or two after dinner, the boy, who was nineteen and an apprentice car mechanic, came indoors from the caravan with a shirt in his hand. It was said that this is what happened. That he asked his mother to sew a button on his shirt, but she said no, she would not do this for him. The boy said nothing and went back to his caravan. Shortly afterwards, he returned to his parents' living room with a rifle and shot them each several times, until they were dead.

Over the years I've thought about this boy, and what could have happened in the life of this family in the time leading up to this terrible event, and I've thought about that night. I've imagined the shirt in his hand, the walk from the living room out to the caravan, the moment of decision, the purposeful steps returning to the back door, up the stairs and through the kitchen, imagined him opening the living room door. What did his parents know, in the moment they saw the raised rifle, about why their son was going to do what he did?

After he killed them – I don't know how long afterwards, but not long – the boy left the rifle in the kitchen, found his car keys and drove his Datsun ten minutes to the home of the man who was his teacher at the technical college. He knocked on the door and the man's wife answered it. She was puzzled – it was nine o'clock at night – but the boy told her he needed to speak with her husband, and something in the way he looked made her understand she must let him in. She called to her husband, who came to the door, and in their kitchen the boy told the teacher what he had done. The teacher took the boy into the living room and sat with him there, and asked his wife to phone the police.

I've thought about this moment too, over the years. The boy, the teacher, the great monstrosity of what he had to say, the numb, slow shock of those minutes passing before the police arrived. The disbelief, the confusion. The kindness of the teacher and his care for the boy. What did they each say, in those fifteen minutes? Did the wife make mugs of hot, very sweet tea? Did they stare at a television screen? What happened in the house of this couple, after the police took the boy away?

Later there was talk of floorboards and blood, and the nonsensical fact of a lost button being the cause of all of this. There was talk of how quiet the young man had been, and of how the parents favoured his older brother, but even then this seemed to me too obvious to be anything but speculation.

There was a preliminary hearing at the local court immediately after the killings. No one came to the court in support of this boy. Not his teacher, and who could blame him? As the police prosecutor read out the charges – murder – the boy sat in the dock, orphaned, sobbing and sobbing into his hands.

Nobody knows the subterranean lives of families.

In the mass today there was talk, of course, of penance and forgiveness. Helen Parry was not there to hear it. I think she was in the town, at the nursing home. I know it's these visits to her mother that have made me remember that boy this morning. Since she told us her mother was still alive, I have remembered more and more instances of Mrs Parry's violence towards Helen, and the grim sadness surrounding every sighting of her in our town.

Helen did not ever surrender to her bullies in the schoolyard, to our teachers, even to our principal. She fought back, spoke up, defied; she spat and swore. But what I have remembered these past days is how unbearably quiet she was in the face of her mother's outbursts. When her mother screamed at her on the bus, or slapped her face outside the supermarket, Helen accepted it, murmuring soothing words or staying altogether silent as the torrent of her mother's rage fell over her, waiting – so still – for the storm to pass. All her senses focused on trying to protect her mother from the shame she was bringing upon both of them.

I left town for university before the boy's trial and did not hear of his sentence, nor whether he would stay in the regional prison located in our town or be taken to live out his sorrowful future in some other town's jail. Maybe he would have preferred to go far away.

~

A few streets away from our town's prison was a garden in which some selected inmates were allowed to work, growing vegetables for use in the prison kitchen. As schoolgirls we would amuse ourselves occasionally by walking past the garden to see the men with rakes and shovels at the rows of cabbages and potatoes. Occasionally one of the girls would call out a greeting or an insult, but the men never looked up. Passing the garden gave us a frisson of danger – there was nothing between us and the men but an ordinary wire fence like those around any farm paddock in the area, and the jail was said to be full of murderers and rapists. But the men permitted to work there seemed downcast and emptied of violence, kneeling between the rows of vegetables in their ugly green tracksuits, or wheelbarrowing weeds to a truck. I suppose there must have been a guard or two somewhere about, but we never saw them. Later, I heard that the men held in our town's prison were mostly child sex offenders, segregated from other criminals for their own safety.

I prayed for (sent compassion, fully attended to) the boy, who would be a man in his early sixties now. I don't think he had any religion back then, but who knew now? I wondered if somewhere, this morning, he too had felt the firm touch of a thumb on his forehead, the dust on his lashes. I assumed at first that he'd still be in prison, but that terrible night was more than forty years ago now, and *life* never really meant life. Perhaps he had been released. What did he think, now, about what he had done? What does it take, to atone, inside yourself? To never be forgiven?

A DEEP CHILL in the air this morning. The first frost, right on time.

~

A friend once told me that her dying brother had summoned a well-known euthanasia campaigner, a doctor, to the house where she and her family were caring for him. Her brother wanted to die, she had no doubt. The doctor made it clear he could not and would not provide 'equipment'; he was there to deliver information only. This was protection against the law. He explained in precise and blunt language the practical options and methods available. 'It was a very sobering conversation,' my friend said. She had hoped to discuss the complexity of the situation with the doctor. She did not want to help her brother die, yet nobody else in the family would agree and he could not do it alone. She didn't tell me the details of what the doctor shared with them, and I did not ask. I knew it was difficult for her to speak of this – it was a summer evening, we were sitting outside in her garden, and other people from the dinner were indoors, laughing at the table. We had come outside to smoke a cigarette. She told me her brother begged her to help him die, and she did. And that she would live with the guilt for the rest of her life.

She told me the doctor who came to help her brother had the coldest manner of any doctor she had ever met. She had seen a lot of surgeons (she'd had cancer years before this, and was now cured), so was well acquainted with the arrogance of doctors. But this man, coming to the house to tell her how to help kill her brother, showed no sympathy or emotion at all.

'He was a very weird guy,' she said. She knew that, morally, he was right to help her brother. She thought him a deeply courageous man, a deeply compassionate man. But in the room with him, she said, his voice and his bearing were not compassionate at all. She said he made her skin crawl. But she listened to what he told her to do, and some days later, when the rest of the family were out, her brother called her to his room. They had agreed this would be the day it would happen, and she did it. Her brother died, and she watched him. Then immediately she destroyed the evidence of what she had done, as instructed, and she called another doctor – a name given to her by the man – and he came to certify the death of her brother.

My friend was dry-eyed as she told me this story. But I could see the cost of what had happened in her face and hear it in her voice. She would never forget and she could never allow herself to feel at ease with what she had done, she told me.

I have seen the doctor on television now and then over the years, and have thought of him with my friend and her brother in the room. It seems clear that he could not have helped her brother if he had the human warmth of ordinary emotion. But in interviews with his friends and family (the wives have come and gone – he is up to wife number four), they describe him as someone with enormous tenderness and humour, and when he himself is interviewed he does show a great deal of wry wit and empathy. I have seen him with tears in his eyes on camera.

I wonder, had the doctor shown compassion or emotion during his visit, whether my friend would have been able to go through with it. Perhaps the coldness was the most compassionate aspect of all. Perhaps this is something that can only be done without any expression of feeling. At her brother's bedside, holding his cooling hand while she waited for the second doctor to come and certify his death, my friend wept and wept and wept. She howled, she said. And when the second doctor came, she took her phone outside and called her siblings and her parents and told them of the death, and she said that with each call she heard her own voice grow colder.

~

In the night I am drawn from sleep by a deep, thrumming rattle. I switch on my bedside lamp and see that the flyscreen over my closed window is crawling with leaping, climbing mice. When the light goes on a shiver goes through the mass, and their scrambling becomes even more frenzied. I turn off the light immediately and lie there rigid, waiting for the noise to stop.

Lying awake in the dark, I understand that this low vibration is telling me a dreadful truth: that I will die. This knowledge that remains mostly hidden from the self but is always there, gaining ground inside us, unstoppable. This is why I hate the mice; I know this now, in the humming darkness. And knowing it doesn't stop the hatred.

I resolve to put the feet of my bed in buckets of deep water as we have been urged to do. I fall back to sleep with the noise still going. They are travelling upwards, to get in through the gaps in the roof.

After this, a dream: I was disconcerted by the suspicion there had been a cockroach scuttling around my room as I slept. A friend came in and, laughing, told me something to turn my insides liquid. She showed me evidence it had not been a cockroach in my room, but a leopard.

~

In the hallway to the dining room hangs the famous Julian of Norwich quotation: *All shall be well, and all shall be well, and all manner of thing shall be well.* Nearby, in a little alcove, hangs something else – a boxed collection of pinned dead butterflies, orange and black, apparently a gift from some old priest of the area, long dead.

I pass these two frames every day, but it happens sometimes here that one is suddenly struck anew by familiar things. During Vigils I am filled with mourning for those butterflies, for all the extinctions and threats, flooded once again with the knowledge that nothing outside these abbey walls is well, and no manner of things shall be well. And I know that inside these walls, Helen Parry is the only one who will face that truth.

And I don't know what my duty is to that knowledge, except to hold it.

RAIN, ALL NIGHT long, beating low and strong on the roof. It's the sound of my early twenties, when I first moved to Sydney and was staggered by the rain that fell so ceaselessly. I came from drought country; I had never seen anything like it. In the city the air indoors was wet, and mould coated our shoes and the backs of our sofas. In one friend's house, water seeped from the walls.

JOSEPHINE HAD A crack at me for remarks I have made at times about my schoolteachers and childhood priests – about the complete absence of women in any of their enthusiastic stories about the Bible or the church. I said in passing a few weeks ago, apparently, that my upbringing showed me that if I didn't hate myself for being a girl, God had no interest in me. I can barely remember saying this, it was so benign to me. But poor Josephine has been stewing on it. She squared up to me yesterday – blushing, of course – and listed important women in the Bible. Ruth and Naomi, she said. And Tamar – 'Judah's shrewd daughter-in-law' – and some other Tamar, daughter of David and 'a victim of family violence'.

'There was even Deborah, *a leader of Israel*,' Josephine said urgently. She asked, what about Jesus' talk with the woman who had been bleeding for twelve years – was that not compassionate? And the Samaritan woman at the well! Women were at the crucifixion; it was *women* who entered the empty tomb of Jesus.

I nodded at Josephine the whole time she was telling me these things, and I felt sorry to have caused this pain in her, so visible as she spoke. I had traduced something she found beautiful and profound, and I know what that feels like, to have something you cherish ridiculed. It's a horrible reduction in your sense of yourself. It makes you feel stupid and ashamed, and I was so sorry to have done that to Josephine.

I apologised for having been so dismissive, and said I could see now that she was right, that there were many powerful female figures in the text. She nodded in a stiff, injured way at my apology. I knew she could tell I couldn't care less about Ruth and her mother-in-law and the Tamars and Deborah, and that were she someone else – Simone, Richard Gittens, even Helen Parry – I might take her on and argue further. Josephine's face took on an even higher colour from knowing that my words were false, and I was sorry again, particularly as it must have been preoccupying her for weeks and weeks. My apology was real, even if the agreement was not.

It makes me embarrassed to lie in this way, and it shows. We parted on good terms but it's there between us now, a knot of real discord, and it won't be easily undone.

Simone looked at me afterwards, and I knew this was the kind of thing she had tried to get me to see in the past. I nodded at her that I understood, and I would try harder.

~

The chickens were ecstatic about being let out into the garden while I worked cleaning out the henhouse. I could hear the mice everywhere among the plants, and the chooks pelted after them, careering through the beds; swerving, savage.

THE RAIN HAS started again, has kept up for days. At first we were hopeful, because it could mean the end of the mice. But it has merely driven them indoors and they are much worse. I stop to speak to Carmel and have to stamp my foot to prevent them scampering over it. Last night, as I sat reading, one *ran up my leg*.

In the church this morning, as I kneeled before the crucifix with a bucket – it was my turn to change the flowers – I noticed a lump on the floor not far away. It was the peaceful dove; it had found its way into the chapel again and must have rammed itself against the big window trying to escape, and hit the floor. But as I moved closer I couldn't help letting out a loud cry. Two mice were busily at work, gnawing at the dove's face. I shrieked and stomped on the floor; the mice fled. The poor bird's black eyes were glossy, and its top beak intact, but from its jaw to its chest was nothing but chewed, bloody gore. I kneeled there by the crucifix and held the cooling, headless creature in my hands. It's the worst desecration yet. My heart would not stop thumping.

WE HAVE MADE a storeroom of one of the most recently reno-
vated, best-sealed guest cabins. There was a brief lull, but now
the mice seem worse than before, as if the plague needed to
rest for a few days to gather its strength. Now we can't store
vegetables in the kitchen at all unless they are in the fridge.

Helen Parry came with me to forage for our meals today. We
unlocked the door (stomping and shouting to scare any mice
from the dark entrance way) and stepped inside. I slammed
the door shut behind us and then we both stood, looking
at the green linoleum covered in pumpkins and swedes and the
window hung with ropes of garlic. The kitchenette benches
and sink house three giant yellow Ikea carry bags filled with
potatoes. Three plastic buckets of brown onions on the desk.
Other vegetables fill the fridge.

We nosed about, checking traps and the cupboards in the cabin. Mercifully there were no mice, and no sign of them yet. We exchanged the hardened lumps of cheese on the traps for fresh ones, or for smudges of peanut butter. Then we stepped silently about the room, filling our plastic baskets with what we need for the week.

In the cabin Helen said to me, 'You remember my mother, don't you.' It was not really a question, as she counted out potatoes and handed them to me from the Ikea bag.

'Yes,' I said, 'I do.' I didn't know what else to say.

Our eyes met for a brief moment. Then Helen nodded and said, 'I thought you would.'

She opened the fridge and lifted out heads of cauliflower and broccoli, and I put them in my basket. On the wall above us, Jesus hung on his cross, sorrowfully keeping watch over this strange harvest.

~

One of the people my mother visited was a woman with such severe depression that she had decided to take her life. How this decision became common knowledge I don't know, but a group of friends arranged a roster of people to stay with her in her house, which was on a property outside town, until she recovered from her illness.

Each morning the visiting friend would rise from bed in the woman's spare room and creep down the hall to wait silently outside her bedroom, listening for movement, to make sure she still lived.

The woman had a terrible sort of patience for these people who wanted to stop her doing what she most wanted. She was not grateful, and she did not allow them to think they were doing a kindness for her, but nor did she send them away. My mother spent the time with her doing jigsaws and looking at gardening books. She would open the curtains so the woman could see her garden, but this was in the middle of winter and the view did not inspire hope. The trees were bare and the frost lay on the ground. Still, they talked softly and my mother made tea, and the woman drank it.

One day the woman said to my mother with light affection, 'Don't worry; I won't do it on one of your days.'

The woman didn't do it on one of my mother's days. Once it was over, my mother said, the friends who had tried to keep the woman alive went back to their families, and the terror of those mornings waiting outside the woman's bedroom was gone. But there was a feeling of catastrophic failure that never went away.

~

I don't think my mother, or anyone else, ever visited Mrs Parry.

OPENING THE CAR door now takes mettle. Bonaventure's lumbar cushion has had to be thrown away. Yesterday I lowered myself too heavily into the seat and felt a squirming sensation at my back that made me roar and hurl myself from the vehicle, twisting my ankle as I did. A dozen mice exploded into the air from behind the cushion, bounced around the driver's seat and footwell trying to escape. It took me twenty minutes to find the courage to get into the car again. Now I open the doors before starting the engine, and wait for them to escape (or hide) before I get in.

~

Some time before I came here for good, my friend Beth received the news of her cancer's incurability, that she would die within one or two years at best, six months at worst. We, her friends, got busy and needy. We called, and sent emails and text messages and cards and flowers. We delivered homegrown vegetables, massage vouchers, food to feed her husband and son when she could not eat herself. We loved her, couldn't bear to lose her. We wanted to do anything we could to save her, though there was nothing to be done. We sent soft clothes, helped her son with homework, raised money for his future education. But we knew the futility of all of it, and a current of panic ran beneath our every attempt to contact her.

Or beneath mine, anyway. I knew it, because I'd felt it before: desperate, bargaining, grasping. Beth could not answer the phone or most messages: she had to conserve her energy. We understood. Of course we understood.

I kept my needfulness to myself, but if I learned another friend had seen her when I had not, I felt almost physically wounded. Not by Beth, for I had no special claim on her, least of all at such a time. But wounded all the same, and desolate, as if something had been taken from me. I suppose it had to do with my mother's illness being the same as Beth's. It's not sophisticated to realise that inside me – in the primitive brain, where real terror lies dormant – that old grief had woken up,

and panic was flooding in. There was a violent feeling of tres-
pass, and that made me ashamed. I spoke to nobody about
this, and made sure to hold myself back from her, limit my
messages, let her be.

On the afternoon I lay with Beth on her soft green lawn –
the same lawn on which she had collapsed with a seizure that
first terrible day – we talked about her life, and what she had
learned. She told me she felt her life had been a lucky one, and
while I could not agree about her luck (there had been many
sorrows in her life), I knew she was telling the truth about her
feelings.

As we lay there, a soft breeze cooling our bare feet, she told
me that someone from her past, a man who had long ago done
something very wrong (she didn't say what) and caused a great
rupture between them, had written to her the day before. He
had reached the ninth step in his twelve-step treatment, and
he wanted to see and speak with her, to *make direct amends*
for what he had done. To complete his treatment and heal,
he needed to right the wrongs he had done her. She laughed
softly as she told me this. She had her son write back to the
man to tell him there was no possibility of them speaking.
The man's approach at this time, wanting her forgiveness,
made her feel sick, she said. She was too tired for anger but
it would not be possible for her to do the work of forgiving
him, or even listening to him. She was no longer capable of

a compassionate lie, she said. In her remaining life there was only room for the truth, and sometimes that would be brutal. It was sad, but it was too late; she had to prepare herself for what was to come. Only what was essential could be allowed to reach her now.

I listened to her speak and did not know how to express my gratitude that she had let me come to see her that day. When she turned her face towards me we saw tears in each other's eyes, and she reached out her hand and I held it, and we lay on our backs on the grass like that, and looked up at the sky while we talked for a little longer. She made me laugh, and I made her laugh – although she was a person who laughed easily, this felt at that moment like the greatest achievement of my life – and then I knew it was time for me to go. We went into the house and she lay on the sofa while I gathered up the bags from the meals I'd brought for her son and husband, and her slobbery old dog followed me to the front door.

I saw her only once after that day. I had been given more than I deserved and it was time for me to step back, make space, ask for nothing. I left food on the doorstep, contributed to a house-cleaner fund, sent funny video clips to her husband. I was always grateful for that hour on the soft grass, that moment of holding her hand. It was only six months, in the end.

Sometimes I think about the man who wanted to make his amends but was rejected. I wonder whether he knew my friend was dying at the time he made his approach, and if he did, what he expected from her. I wonder if he was sorry for not offering to make amends in the long decades before she became sick. I think about his living out the rest of his life knowing she died without accepting his apology or granting forgiveness, and I think how that kind of regret might never leave a person.

I suppose they tell you to expect this, in twelve-step programs. I imagine there are a lot of people who don't want to hear those apologies, who want nothing to do with your amends. Who say: too late, too late.

~

A feeling that something is coming, waiting to be born, out of this time. Almost physical, like before a period, or a pregnancy, or vomiting. Something is getting ready to resolve itself.

HELEN PARRY FOLLOWED me to the chook house this morning. She held out her hand and I had no choice but to place a fresh egg in her palm. I kept about my business, ducking my head into the shed to reach into the laying boxes, pushing under a warm hen to draw out the eggs. One by one she kept taking them from me.

After filling her pockets with the eggs, Helen stood and surveyed me there in my overalls, as I unlatched the feed bin and scooped out the pellets, scattered them on the dirt. The chickens rushed at it and I stood in a pool of feathers.

She asked if she could come with me next time I went into town. I said yes, of course she could. All day afterwards, at the thought of going to our town with Helen Parry, I felt a hard, rough little kernel of tension, like a peach pit, in my chest.

~

My parents were members of a small community group dedicated to the 'resettlement' of twenty or so refugees who had fled the Vietnam War, travelled by boat to Australia and somehow, after this arduous, life-threatening journey, ended up living in our town. I don't know whether they had a choice about where they lived – our town seemed as far from Vietnam as it was possible to get. Perhaps that was the point.

I don't remember anyone speaking to us children about what they had endured, and we certainly had little to no idea about the war going on in Vietnam, but we had seen refugees on the television news for years, the screaming babies and exhausted families – the women so thin and young it seemed impossible they could be mothers – climbing from ragged boats onto dry land.

The families my parents befriended were extremely quiet people, except for one jovial man who often spoke on behalf of others, asking for what they needed. The group of townspeople found them houses to live in, jobs, furniture and clothes. Occasionally my parents would be invited to their homes for a celebration dinner, consisting of many small dishes of things we'd never seen before. There is a photograph of my father, by then grown pudgy, in the centre of a group of Vietnamese men who are laughing. One of the men is pretending to feed my father from his own bowl, and the joke is that my father, the only white man, is some kind of emperor. This was thought funny back then. The men in the picture appear to be enjoying themselves, but who knows what they really thought. I have always assumed this posing would not have been my father's idea, rather a joke initiated by one of the men. But perhaps I'm wrong. I wonder if any of *their* children, as they grew up, saw a copy of that same photograph. I can imagine them looking at my father with hatred. I would too.

Occasionally a new family would arrive in town and the process of finding homes, work and so forth would begin again. There would be a barbecue lunch on a farm to welcome them, and show them what the real Australia looked like. Once, two tiny girls who had been separated from their parents came to be in our care for a few days. They were about three and four years old. I can't think now what horrors these children had already endured, to end up in our house, silent and afraid. We spoke to them softly, and did not know how to comfort them, but my mother and father held them gently and put them to bed together, fed them, bathed them. I sang them nursery rhymes – 'Twinkle Twinkle, Little Star', 'Mary Had A Little Lamb', in hope that the gentleness of my voice would help them know they were safe. We took them to one of the parties out on a farm, where they would be taken into the care of other Vietnamese people. Soon they would have someone speak to them in their own language. We tried to convey this as we drove, our voices low, smiling at them lovingly. They sat mute on the back seat of the car with me, their tiny legs sticking straight out.

But once the car turned onto the road out of town, the little girls became terrified at what they saw out of the window – simply the bare, ordinary, dry paddocks – and hurled themselves to the floor behind the driver's seat, sobbing and crying out, curling up very tight and clutching each other. I had never seen real terror before. We had no idea what was wrong, tried to tell them there was no danger. My father kept driving, speaking quietly, and I lay across the seat, stroking the little girls' hair and murmuring that no harm would come to them. Eventually we arrived at the place, and they were taken from the car by Vietnamese adults, who took them into their arms and patted and soothed them as they cried.

Later, my parents said the girls had been thrown into terror because to them open countryside represented some dreadful danger – landmines, or bombs. I don't know if this was true, or just some explanation they invented to make sense of what had happened. I remember that we drove home in silence, without the small girls, and saw our flat Monaro paddocks differently.

When I was about thirteen, I took my friend Kelly along to another gathering, this time a garden party for some new arrivals. I was sick of these occasions by now – of being polite to the homeowner strangers, and sick of the great opaque force of horror and trouble that had forced the Vietnamese families to make new lives in our town, and of what felt like the uncrossable oceans of difference between us. Not that I ever asked for or was given any details about them or their journeys here; I was too wrapped up in my own life to care. Kelly and I slouched about the lunch table, avoiding the Vietnamese food, picking out sausage rolls and party pies and taking our stacked little plates to a corner of the yard where we sat on the grass watching the people we knew and making sarcastic comments about them. But my mother called us back to the group to meet a very young couple, only a few years older than Kelly and me. Their names were Binh and Thuy, and they were – we assumed – boyfriend and girlfriend. They seemed happy to see some other young people, and smiled widely, said hello in English, and then giggled when we asked how they were. They could only say, 'Hello pleased to meet you.' We – of course – had learned no Vietnamese phrases at all. But the open friendliness of the couple led us to begin miming a kind of conversation, which had us all laughing and calling, 'Ah!' in recognition when we understood. The afternoon opened into beauty for Kelly and me. We led the couple away from the larger group and showed them things, teaching them the names of objects, and they teaching us in turn. *Leaf. Jeans. Hair. Plate.* By the end of the day, we felt something serious and true had taken place. We hugged them goodbye – they seemed a little taken aback – and there was a lot of smiling and waving, and repeating of 'leaf' and 'plate'. I had a sense of some moral blossoming inside me, where it was possible not just to endure such occasions in awkward embarrassment but to find pleasure and freshness there.

Two weeks later, in the street with some of my other friends – not Kelly but louder girls, whose parents were normal, and who sometimes used insults about the Vietnamese people that my mother and father forbade in our house – I saw Binh and Thuy outside a shop across the road. They were so thin, and their charity shop clothes drooped on their delicate bodies. Their sneakers looked enormous, comical, on their fine feet. They saw me too, and their faces lit up. 'Hello!' they called, their smiles bright, hands raised in greeting.

I couldn't help them. Here in the bright street with my schoolfriends, I could not. I nodded, gave a low, half-waggle of my hand and a pinched smile. I turned away from them, marched on with my friends, my head down, sick with shame.

Of course, as soon as we had left the party Kelly and I forgot the Vietnamese words Binh and Thuy taught us.

HELEN PARRY SAT in the passenger seat with the window wound down, surfing her hand up and down the cold air as we drove. She didn't look at me, but out of the window, as we rattled across the cattle grid and I turned right, away from the paint-ball place and past the little grey hall. Past the Gittenses', onto the road into town.

I found myself telling her something I had not told anyone before. That on the first day I ever came to the abbey, as I drove through the edge of town, past the broken-down old museum and the stone courthouse which now seemed much smaller than I remembered, I saw a man slip into a drain and disappear.

I told Helen Parry that as I drove I noticed – idly, without paying real attention – that at the side of the road a man was sitting at the opening of a large stormwater drain, his legs

261

dangling down into the space. And then, just as I passed him, almost before I'd registered what I had seen, he dropped from sight – body, head and shoulders and then two gripping hands – into the drain. In my next glance – a double take into the rear-vision mirror – there was nothing to see but an ordinary car parked at the side of the road. The day was dry. The drain was built into the road's kerbing. No lid had been moved; there would be nothing to show where the man had gone.

He had to have known what he was doing, lowering himself inside so nimbly. Probably he was some kind of service worker, though he didn't look like one – there was no high-vis gear or equipment. No council truck or van. I kept driving, slowly, but looked back repeatedly to see if he would re-emerge. Perhaps I'd made a mistake and it had not actually happened, but I knew it had, as I watched the abandoned car grow smaller in my mirror. He'd vanished, and although other vehicles soon passed me from the opposite direction, I knew I was the only one on this earth who had seen him disappear.

As a person often does when they see something strange, I told Helen Parry, I decided that there was nothing wrong with this picture, and I drove on. I forgot about him within a few kilometres, spent the rest of the trip concentrating on the road, on the directions I'd been given, and on looking for the turn-off that would bring me eventually to the sisters' place. But, I said now, over the years since I've sometimes thought about that man, that moment of the drop, and what he thought would happen next.

'You decided that he wanted to disappear,' Helen said, still gazing out of her side window. 'Yes,' I said. Then she said: 'Like you.'

I drove, thinking about her words and that decision I seem to have made, in the middle of my life. Choosing disappearance, while Helen has chosen the opposite. I thought about the costs of those decisions, for each of us.

We were coming to the hill just then, where our old high school still stood. 'Can you stop here?' Helen Parry asked, and I slowed the car and pulled in alongside the tall granite buildings and the thick stone fence. It was a school day. The tuckshop roller door and the entrance to the school office were both open. We saw no movement, no students or teachers walking about, but we knew they were inside, sitting at desks or standing before the class.

The room in which we had had our sewing lessons was not visible from the street. I could have no idea what was going through Helen Parry's mind. My heart thrummed, but she said nothing. I had kept the engine going, but now I thought perhaps Helen wanted to get out and to go into the grounds; maybe she would ask me to go with her and if she did, I would have to agree to do this. I was about to turn the engine off when she said, 'Okay,' and she nodded at the road to indicate we should start driving again. I wanted to reach out to touch her arm, but I didn't do that. Instead, I continued into the town and the car park of the supermarket, and as we got out of the car Helen told me she would meet me here in half an hour, and she walked off away from me.

After the shopping, as I waited for Helen Parry to come back, I thought about the Country Women's Association meeting I had once attended in our town, to give a fundraising speech. This was when I was an adult but before my mother was ill. I had come to see my mother and, while I was there, I agreed to speak on behalf of the threatened species centre. It was the usual about-us/why-care spiel, a careful mix of reality and some slender confected 'hope', with a few local examples, facts and figures thrown in. This was around the time of some debate over whether to cull feral horses in the national park, and people were angry at what they saw as animal cruelty. They loved the brumbies, which they said were part of local culture and history. It was the stuff of famous poetry and a famous film, of bushman identity. The imagery of wild horses running free stirred something deep and patriotic. It was difficult to argue for the threatened native species – the northern and southern corroboree frogs, the anemone buttercup, the Monaro golden daisy, the alpine she-oak skink and mountain pygmy possum, many others. I tried, but by the end of my talk I knew from the resentment on their faces that I had failed.

Before my speech there was a discussion about the local hospital and its need for services for patients with eating disorders. On the panel were a local doctor, a women's health psychiatrist from Canberra and the parents of a young woman from the town who had died from an eating disorder. The doctor spoke of the need for a separate treatment unit, and the number and kind of girls – they were almost always girls at that time – who needed help. The psychiatrist told the women in the audience about the latest research on intervention for bulimia, anorexia and other forms of disordered eating. At the back of the room, seated next to some of the townspeople, I listened and was reminded of my school friend Dimitra, who could not bear for the different foods on her plate to touch. She would spend a portion of every mealtime carefully separating mashed potato from meat, peas from gravy, with her knife. We, her friends, laughed at her. We thought it was something weird only she did.

When the time came for the parents to speak, the room quietened. The mother was a short, ordinary-looking woman with a blonde bob and a smooth face, while the father looked – deranged. A stillness descended on the women in the room. We watched the mother swallow before standing, and put on her reading glasses as she stepped forward to the micro-phone. Her voice was very quiet as she gave the details of how and when her daughter's problem began. The mother held a framed photograph of the dead girl, face out, the whole time she spoke in her soft wavering voice.

I watched the women around me, their attention absolutely fixed on the mother. The girl in the picture was a healthy teenager, but the mother described the increasing horror of the illness. Sometimes in the faces of my fellow audience members I thought I could see a hint of scepticism, along with the sympathy and half-buried fear; they had daughters of their own. The mother of the girl spoke so softly, we had to concentrate hard to hear her. At that time parents were often blamed for such illnesses. The parents of anorexics were seen as rigid and controlling, and the parents of bulimics as chaotic. We used those terms back then – *anorexics, bulimics*.

The family's property was on the outskirts of town near a football oval, and by the time the girl was first hospitalised at seventeen, the mother said, she and her husband were taking it in turns to sleep on her bedroom floor in order to stop her from rising in the middle of the night, pulling on her sports shoes and making her way down to the oval, where she would run around and around until morning. Eventually, after many hospitalisations, she died at nineteen and a half.

The mother spoke about pressure from society, about judgemental medical care and body-image distortion. If the family had more information, less isolation, if her daughter had been given specialised help, in her own town, she might still be alive.

When the mother sat down, a river of relief moved through the women in the audience, and people turned to give each other looks of sadness.

Then the father stood up, and the room tensed. The man was known in this town. He was from no family around here, and had bought the property when it was overgrazed and eroded. He was reputed to be a soil scientist, but he worked for nobody, and ran his property using strange water-management methods nobody had heard of back then, and gradually the land improved, though nobody visited to find out why or how. They would not have been welcome. He was a man known to cause a ruckus – in shops, in council meetings. He had declared that all four of his children would be homeschooled, and his wife – previously the manager of a pharmacy in town – quit her job to teach them. This had caused more suspicion. Were our schools, our children, not good enough for theirs? The ill daughter had been extraordinarily intelligent, and despite the homeschooling and the hospitalisations her marks had been among the state's highest in the year twelve leaving certificate.

The father said, 'I disagree with my wife on several points as to the cause of our daughter's illness. I agree with her that we need better treatment.'

The mother clasped the picture of the girl in her lap and looked mildly at the floor beside her crossed ankles. She appeared unsurprised at what was to come; she looked at the floor, and then up at the noticeboard on the wall beside the tea urns, with the same expression you might wear looking out of the window on a familiar train journey.

The father didn't believe their daughter had low self-esteem or perfectionism or distorted body image. 'Annabel was sickened by the state of this world,' he said, looking at the back of the room. I could hear anxious inhalations around me. He did not believe that societal sexism was to blame; he did not believe his daughter was so vapid as to starve herself because she didn't look like a model. She was not punishing herself for failing her cold and rigid parents. The fact was that Annabel was so disgusted by greed, by the ruination of the natural world because of it, that, like ascetics before her, the only action she could take was to remove herself, bit by bit, from the obscenity of this excess.

'Her suffering was an existential and a moral problem,' he said. 'Not a medical one.'

There seemed the taint of mockery in the way he said the word *medical*. The doctor and the psychiatrist sat in their chairs, watching him carefully. The doctor looked at the back of the man's head, and chewed up his bottom lip a little, the way some people do when they are trying to work out a puzzle. The psychiatrist held one of her hands tightly with the other in her lap. Apart from these small movements, both seemed very careful to maintain neutral expressions. I wondered if they had known the man would say these things. As the man spoke, the women around me were beginning to fidget and murmur. They did not like to see the doctor and the psychiatrist insulted in this way. They did not want to hear lectures about greed and excess from a man who could not protect his own child.

The man said that his daughter sacrificed her own life out of revulsion for capitalism, for the consumption responsible for the unprecedented collapse of ecosystems, the galloping extinctions – but at this the audience could take no more. They made their offence obvious, jostling their chairs and muttering, and a voice from the middle of the room said, 'Oh, come *on*.' Just before he stepped back from the microphone the man said, 'And I respect my daughter for that decision.'

When he said this there was gasping. A number of women near me in the audience *hissed*.

I did not like the man, but nor did I despise him as these women did. I did not find it difficult to believe what he said about his daughter. He seemed unperturbed by the room's response.

It's been my observation over many years that those who most powerfully resist convention quite peaceably accept the state of being reviled.

~

As a child, I was lightly embarrassed at my mother's disdain for the CWA, when my friends' mothers went to meetings there, made cakes for their fundraisers, knitted. My mother said it was simply 'not for me'. And she was not good at making fairy cakes or even fruitcakes, though she made plenty of dry scones that I liked.

When she was ill, in the hours we spent in hospital waiting rooms, passing the time with meandering conversation, I asked her about the CWA for some reason. She told me that as a young bride she had dutifully turned up to a meeting there, in about 1961. The topic of discussion, she said, arching an eyebrow, was the wording of a letter protesting the fact that women's trouser manufacturers had moved zippers from the side *to the front*. She could not remember who the letter was supposed to go to, nor what the actual problem with the front zipper was supposed to be, but she presumed it must have represented *easier access to you-know-what*. 'I quietly left and never went back.' We laughed softly together in the pale spearmint gloom of the hospital corridor.

I thought of both these occasions – the girl's unwelcome father at one, my mother removing herself from a different one – as I sat waiting for Helen Parry in the car park beside the old CWA hall, now a kickboxing studio, in our town.

When Helen came back to the car she dropped into her seat and pulled shut the door, and then she turned to me and said, 'I've got a flight out, next week.' For the first time, I saw her smile.

I told her I was glad for her. And I was glad, not just for her but for all of us. Yet I felt something old and familiar, the feeling I'd had in the forest, of incompletion.

Then, as I drove out of the car park, Helen Parry asked shyly, 'Can you do me a favour?' She asked me to drive back a different way, and she named the streets she wanted me to follow, and I said I could, and I drove her along the roads of our town. We stopped on a hill outside the block of what had once been housing commission flats, and she got out of the car and stood in the cement driveway, looking up at the high narrow windows of the top floor for a time, while I waited in the car.

I thought of the electrical cord from the kettle and the too-tight uniform and the way Helen would be left to care for herself for weeks at a time. I thought of the public slappings and shouting.

Helen stood with her hands in her jacket pockets in the wind, and then she came and let herself back into the car. And all I wanted was to drive right away from that building and from whatever had happened to Helen in it. So I did. I drove us away, away – but just as I was about to turn back onto the highway out of town, Helen said, 'Go left,' and I realised she wanted us to take the road that ran past the town's hospital.

I had not driven this road since I left town myself, but now I did as Helen Parry asked. As the building loomed up in front of us she said, 'Turn in here,' and I eased the car over the lip of the hospital driveway. We drove through the car park to the far exit, and then we coiled slowly around the hospital's narrow one-way road. We passed its maternity wing, where we both had been born, passed its children's ward and its newer additions, the breast-screening place and X-ray and pathology centres, and then we looped past the adult wards containing the room in which my father had died (my beautiful father!), with my mother at his bedside. I was breathing light, shallow breaths, and beside me I could feel the strain in Helen's body too.

She said, very softly, 'Okay.'

I understood this meant I should stop the car, and I saw that we were coming to the end of a long strip of road, where it bulged into a turning circle before a group of small buildings a good distance from the rest of the hospital. I stopped the car at the edge of this turning circle, where a few parking spaces were provided. Ahead of us were some brick blocks with security grilles on the doors. Helen Parry sat in her seat and looked for a long time at those doors. She breathed the same shallow breaths as I did. Beside the buildings was a little dried-out attempt at a garden, and a low wooden sign carved with the name DHURRAWAN and below that its translation:

LIGHT. It was the kind of use authorities tended to make of Aboriginal languages when they didn't want to be explicit about what something was, which in this case was the mental health unit.

In our childhood this place was called something else, and the name of it was used as an insult. Nobody we knew had been near it, but occasionally we heard gothic tales from someone's mother's friend who was a cleaner, or a father who delivered hospital linen there. We joked about padded cells and strait-jackets and Nurse Ratched.

The icy wind was still blowing as we sat there in the car, and I remembered the colour of the sea water once after a terrible flood, when I lived near the ocean. For many weeks rubbish washed up on the beach, even though the floods had happened a long way away. I would go to the sea each after-noon and drag what rubbish I could grasp out of the shallows, up the beach and into the car park, to leave beside the bins. I dragged out part of a huge household water tank, a big piece of heavy black pipe, a bright orange traffic bollard and panels of fridges and ovens, broken sofa frames. Out of the surf I pulled a brown plastic chair and the inside panelling of a car door, hauling them across the sand to leave them dripping on the car park bitumen. But every time I looked back at the ocean after taking away as much rubbish as I could, I saw that the water still roiled and rocked with debris – frightening black branches and other dark shapes, and I saw that the water itself was a horrible purplish colour. I thought of that colour as *evil*, a word I never used. But that was what it looked like to me, the sea in its unnatural colour and turmoil, with the claws of broken trees now and then showing themselves in the water then disappearing again.

I sat in the car with Helen Parry as she watched the locked doors of those closed buildings, and I understood that when her mother had left her alone for weeks at a time, this was where she had been. And nobody in our town – not a teacher, a psychiatrist or doctor or nurse, not a schoolmate, another parent, not Mrs Bird nor my mother – had made a move to do anything about a schoolgirl left on her own in a housing commission flat, getting herself to school each day to be insulted and assaulted and despised, going home at the end of the day alone.

One of the security grille doors opened and a young woman stepped out. A nurse, in her uniform of blue pants and a plain blue smock. She wore an orange lanyard around her neck, a plastic security tag with a set of keys dangling from it. She shut the security door behind her and pulled it to make sure it was locked, and then stepped out into the wind. As she passed our car she saw us watching and gave us a smile – an extraordinarily gracious, warm smile, it felt to me – which passed through the glass into the space here in our car, and then she trotted past us to another building.

A spell was broken. Helen turned to me and said, 'Let's go.' And I drove the car away from the locked buildings, past the maternity centre where at this very moment women would be pacing the halls, or butting their heads into their husband's chests, or crouching on all fours giving birth, and we drove out into the cold streets.

We had one more stop to make.

I waited in the car while Helen went into the aged-care centre for one last visit. She stayed in there a long time. I dozed in a slant of sunlight coming into the car, despite the buffeting of the wind. I woke when the passenger door opened, and Helen got back inside and clipped her seatbelt. She didn't say anything, but there was in her expression something resolved, concluded.

As we drove through the streets of our town again she said quietly, 'I need you to know that I loved my mother, and she – tried, as much as she was able, to love me.'

It seemed important to repeat her words aloud. I did, and I said I was glad Helen knew this, about herself and her mother. And then we drove out of our town, along the highway, up the steep road coiling through the bush and then out the other side, across the top of the high, stony, windblown plains.

~

There is something called forgiveness therapy, I have read. Psychologists working in this field say that true forgiveness cannot take place without detailed, thorough assessment and acknowledgement of the nature and effect of the injury. Forgiveness, they say, does not require reconciliation with the person who has caused the harm, nor does it mean forgetting the hurt.

There are four steps to true forgiveness, the therapists say: uncovering the nature of the harm; the decision phase, in which to explore whether to grant forgiveness or withhold it; the necessary 'work'; and the final step, deepening or discovery. Many people reach the decision phase and find that it is not possible to forgive after all. In the work phase, the injured person must labour to understand the individual who caused the harm in a new way, which may create more compassion towards the offender and oneself. In the final deepening stage, the forgiver is supposed to find the hurt and hatred associated with the injustice receding even further. The forgiver may discover meaning in their suffering, and understand that there is a freedom in forgiveness.

This is serious work, beyond the reach of occasion or rhetoric. And it is not for any individual to urge such rigorous, such dangerous and painful moral work upon another.

~

When we got back from town, the sound of Richard Gittens's excavator was grinding out across the paddocks once again. Helen went to her cabin and I walked to the fence, but the digger was not visible anywhere near the mouse pit. The sound came from some distance away, from beyond the dam. Then the bell sounded, and I made my way to the church.

~

After my friend Beth died, I sometimes felt that I had invented our closeness, or exaggerated it, for I knew people who had spent years in her company, who had been her friends since before her child was born, and although I had known her a long time we were not close until those last few years. Her old friends knew each other well; they gathered to cry and mourn. But I wasn't in their circle and I did not want to intrude on their grief, so I stayed away from those occasions.

When I realised I had lost or deleted Beth's text and voice messages, the way one does over time, I cried. I searched and searched my computer and my phone for any trace of her, but there was none. But I had one thing: a panel from a cardboard box in which she had given me a bottle of champagne,

277

for a small professional favour I'd done her. She wrote on it her thanks, and added, *You are a true and generous friend.* I tore the panel from the box and kept it for many years, and when I felt estranged from the memories of my time with her I would hunt out the piece of cardboard and read this message again. She wrote this, I would think. She did.

THIS MORNING A fine, delicate layer of ice formed on the water in the glass beside my bed: winter has come early.

The courtyard is filthy with muck and leaves, cobwebs powdery with dust. All through the psalms I kept thinking of a broom, longing for the feel of it in my hands. Afterwards I found one in the shed. I bashed its bristles on the low brick wall to empty it of spiders, strode into the yard and went at it. The deep satisfaction of swept pavers and bricks, their stern beauty and order restored. As I swept it came to me that my inability to get over my parents' deaths has been a source of lifelong shame to me. I used to think that time, adulthood, would clean it away, but no. It recedes sometimes but then it returns and I'm eternally stuck; a lumbering, crying, self-pitying child. The fact of grief quietly making itself known, again and again.

~

Nobody has seen a living mouse in two days, though we still come across half-eaten bodies here and there, making us yelp.

~

In the last weeks and days of my mother's life, I played music to fill the hours. My mother knew she was dying, although once the news of this inevitability had been delivered by the doctor, and I saw her blinking, trying to take in what had been said, we didn't speak of it again. What would there have been to say? She accepted and adapted in her quiet way, as she always had in the face of catastrophe.

It could not have been simple. She must surely have wept. But if she did, she was so private about it I never saw, though I was with her almost all the time.

This time was in the middle of winter, and her bedroom faced out over her garden and a dogwood tree bare of leaves or flowers. Sometimes I'm sorry she didn't die in spring, when she could have been accompanied by a vision of light green leaves, and banks of irises and daisies and hollyhocks, and the sound of bees in the dogwood blossom. But perhaps that would have made the leaving of her life even more painful. As it was, green leaves were not what she saw from her window.

Winter in our town is a bleak and unforgiving time, and her view was a monochrome of sticks, bare branches, dead lawn and an icy grey sky. A blanket of snow might have softened this view, but snow never fell; only sleet, or sharp spattering rain falling in gusts of wind.

People came and went a great deal in those last weeks, saying their goodbyes. Sometimes she was able to sit in a small patch of surprise warmth in a corner of what was hopefully called 'the sunroom', but she was increasingly weak and unable to move from her bed. Palliative care nurses came once or twice a day, subtly blessing the house with their supreme competence and their kindness. I came to think of these women as sainted, though I know they disliked language like that. I think they found the language of religion somehow condescending, or silly, and I never said anything like this aloud. I heard other people call them 'angels' and I can see why that grated, too, with its mawkish evocations of mysticism, when their skill was not miraculous but medical, intellectual, hard-earned. And yet . . . there was also some other, instinctive giftedness in their work. They seemed to recede when others were in the room, making way for grieving and goodbyes, but never abandoning me or their patient. They filled the morphine syringe in its driver with smooth efficiency, untangled tubes, showed me how to turn her, how to moisten her lips and mouth.

Even when barely conscious, my mother received her tearful visitors with a pale, transcendent solemnity, growing smaller and more skeletal there in her bed, but also enlarging in some way – I suppose I mean spiritually. She seemed to rise, even as she shrank. I could never have said this to anyone. I don't know what has caused me to want to say it now.

Through these days I played music I thought my mother would like: Bach, and Debussy, some Beethoven piano sonatas. Sometimes when she was fast asleep – she slept longer and more deeply as the weeks went by, although how did one tell the difference between sleep and unconsciousness? – I played my own music, randomly choosing something from the pile of CDs I had brought in from my car when I arrived.

Once I went into her room when she had woken up, and I could see she was listening, her head heavy on the pillow but her eyes soft. She parted her dry lips and murmured, indicating she would like to hear again the song that had just been playing, which was REM's 'Everybody Hurts'. She asked to hear it again almost every day until she lost consciousness for good.

When your day is long
And the night, the night is yours alone

~

Before this time, when she was recovering from her surgery in the middle of a hot summer while staying in the spare room of my dingy inner-city apartment, she grew irrationally but profoundly anxious about certain things. In this first-floor apartment there lived two cats who liked to prowl the wide windowsills, sidling elegantly past the open windows as they had done for years. The windows stayed open all summer, for there was no air conditioning and without the cross-breeze the apartment, which faced the western sun, was unbearably hot. Once I phoned my doctor – the same one who had told me about the bedrock, and who had also treated my mother for various horrible effects of her illness that her surgeon couldn't fix, and in which he therefore showed no interest – and I explained to her that my mother was growing obsessively worried about the cats. That she was frightened, terrified indeed, that the cats would fall from the open windows and be killed. She pleaded with me to close the windows, seemingly more frightened of the cats coming to harm than of anything to do with her own situation, and I did close them when she was in the room, but her anxiety continued even then, and in the hot stillness she would be constantly glancing at the windows, her eyes glassy with fear.

The doctor told me she was writing a prescription for a tranquilliser and that I could come to the surgery and collect it within the hour. Thinking of this now, I find it remarkable that I never took any of the pills myself.

In all the time of her illness my mother confessed only one other fear to me, when we were sitting in a hospital corridor as she waited for some kind of scan, a few days before her surgery. She was very, very frightened of having 'a near-death experience'. She had read things, and heard things, about the light, the tunnel, about being drawn blissfully towards death but then returning. The thought of it filled her with dread. There was nothing I could say to comfort her, and after she had made this confession she spoke of it no more, withdrawing into herself. After the operation I asked her about it and she seemed a little sheepish, but I could tell she was relieved. There had been no experience but a kind anaesthetist and instant oblivion, and for that we were both grateful.

I wish, for the thousandth time that I had been older than I was when she fell ill. I feel sure more maturity would have brought with it some greater capacity to help her than I had.

~

Today Simone told us all at the midday dinner that Helen Parry is leaving us. Helen smiled as Sissy and Carmel and Bonaventure and the others made noises of exclamation and gladness, unable to hide that the gladness was not for Helen, as they said, but for themselves, and for us.

A car will come for Helen in two days, and her flight to Bangkok will leave in three.

Bonaventure watched Simone then as she made another announcement: Richard Gittens has excavated a grave for the bones in the Stone Yard paddock on the far side of the dam, and Sister Jenny can finally be laid to rest. We will do this before Helen Parry leaves.

~

I asked my mother, near the end, if she was afraid of dying. She looked past me, through the window to the dogwood, and said in a quiet, even voice that she was 'a bit nervous'. Later I would tell this story with pride in my mother's stoicism and accept-ance, her bravery, her strange faith (she said, another time, that she was looking forward to seeing my father, and her brother, wherever she was going; but she also said she did not believe in heaven or hell or an afterlife of any kind). Then I read in a novel these words: '"Nervous" was Papa's word for terror.'

~

Once, when I was married, Alex woke me at five in the morning, in trouble. He said, I think I'm having some sort of allergic reaction. His face was very swollen and his voice was thick, and he said he was finding it hard to swallow water. I gave him antihistamines that he did swallow, with difficulty, and I called an ambulance while standing naked in the kitchen. I dressed myself while I spoke to the operator, in Alex's sweater, which was hanging on a stair post, and a pair of tights from the laundry basket. In around twenty minutes the ambulance arrived and took my husband to the hospital.

I have never told anyone that almost as soon as he told me he was having trouble with his breathing – his tongue was thickening and his throat beginning to constrict – I had an urgent need to use the toilet, an urge I ignored while I called the ambulance and watched my husband's red face, and we waited to see the flashing lights coming down the hill. The whole time I spoke to the triple zero operator I felt the need to use the bathroom, and I controlled the need. I felt completely calm the whole time: during the call; while I gave Alex the two antihistamine pills and watched him swallow them; while I dressed in my strange outfit; while I went out onto the road to wave the ambulance down in the sunrise. I did not have a racing heartbeat at any time, I did not sweat or stammer.

As soon as they took Alex away in the ambulance, and I knew they were caring for him, and I knew he would recover – I would follow them to the hospital in my car momentarily – I could no longer control this need. I went to the toilet and sat down and my bowels emptied completely. This is not pleasant to talk about I know, but it happened: an urgent, steady, total voiding, the need for which had insisted on itself as soon as I knew my husband was in danger. This went on for some time, and I could do nothing to stop it. I sat with my elbows on my knees, my head in my hands, letting my body empty itself, until there could be nothing left. Throughout the hour of this emergency I had been absolutely calm. But the primitive body knows fear, and responds.

I have had this same thing happen two or three times in my life, at moments of great crisis, and I have never spoken of it to anyone.

IT'S VERY COLD, and raining lightly on the morning we bury the bones.

It took me a day or so to understand that permission from the local authorities still hasn't come and isn't likely to anytime soon. There will be no priest, no Church permission either. I remembered Helen Parry coming down from the Stone Yard that day at the dam. It was Helen who found the place, who talked to Richard, who broke through the despair of inaction by showing us we could give permission to ourselves.

This is what takes place. At ten o'clock Richard Gittens comes in his LandCruiser, and then six of us – Josephine and Sissy at the head, Bonaventure and Simone in the centre, Dolores and me at the feet – slide the coffin of Sister Jenny off the trestle table and onto an old tea trolley. Together we guide the casket out of the room and down the hallway, half-carrying it by its rope handles, lest its weight be too much and overbalance its flimsy vehicle. Carmel walks ahead of us, moving hall tables and chairs out of our path, telling us where to slow down to manoeuvre our way across the curled edge of the hall runner, and carefully watching the tea trolley's little castors to make sure they do not buckle under the casket's weight. They do not.

At the front door Richard meets us. He helps us lift the casket into the back of his vehicle, which he has reversed all the way to the step. He closes the tailgate and bolts it, and covers the coffin with an old blanket before securing it with ratchet tiedowns, and then with Simone and Bonaventure in the cabin beside him he drives slowly off behind the sheds, from the home paddock to Nursery, through the next paddock and the next, with Simone getting out to open and close the gates each time. They drive from Nursery through Dungeon and on, to the gravesite Helen has chosen on the side of a hill in Stone Yard, with a single ribbon gum nearby and a view down to the abbey and across the plains. The rest of us follow on foot – the four of us and Helen Parry – and then I see that Annette Gittens is here too, making this sombre walk, all of us in our heavy shoes and rain jackets or carrying umbrellas, moving across the paddocks in the spitting rain.

It takes us twenty-five minutes to reach the site where Richard has parked, beside the excavator and the dark hole in the earth. A ladder is in place, and it is a shock when Richard Gittens and Helen Parry climb down into the pit. The rest of us kneel at the graveside, and we nudge and lever, gently manoeuvring Sister Jenny's coffin into their outstretched arms. There is a moment, a communal intake of breath, when it seems the coffin will fall, but Helen's and Richard's arms and backs are strong, and they do not falter as they adjust, and lower, and lay Jenny's bones down into the earth. Then they inch themselves along, their backs against the soil walls, to the end of the pit. First Richard and then Helen climb the ladder that Bonaventure and I are holding steady. Bonaventure takes Richard's arm as he steps onto the grass, and then he holds the ladder and I take Helen's arm and pull her out, away from the grave. We grip each other's elbows strongly, and then I look into her brown eyes and she looks into mine for a moment. We tighten, then loosen our holds and let each other go.

The ladder is lifted out and all of us stand around the open grave, heads bowed, the rain pattering down on our plastic coats. We close our eyes and Simone commits the body of her – our – sister to the earth. May rest now, real rest at last, be granted to Jenny, and may a perpetual light shine upon her. There is a little quiet crying. May our trespasses be forgiven, may we forgive them. I do not look for Helen, but I know she knows I ask it; and I know too that she has other, deeper forgivenesses to consider, or to decide against.

Afterwards we take turns to throw shovelfuls of earth down on the bones of Jenny. It is a surprise that Annette takes a turn, her face streaming with tears for her own old and private pain, and she leans into Richard's chest and he stands, in mourning, with his arms around his wife. By now it is raining harder, the earth turning muddy. Simone says something to Richard, and then we are standing back, holding each other's hands, as Richard starts up the excavator and the machine trundles forward and pushes the earth – all the earth – back into its rightful place. Beyond the excavator, in the distance, I see Helen already making her way back across the paddocks.

Afterwards, as we walk through the wet grass with sodden shoes and feet, I look down to the buildings; the figure of Helen Parry is ferrying bags and boxes from her cabin to the opened hatch of a black car waiting for her in the drive. By the time we reach the last gate, she has gone.

LYING IN BED in the dark morning. At last, after all these weeks, the rain has really stopped and the birds are out, and I can hear the burbling of the chickens. The mouse plague, it seems, is finished for now.

A memory comes of my childhood dog, Peggy – a dusty three-legged kelpie-cross whom my parents had found injured on the road after she had been hit by a car, before I was born. They took her to the vet, where her injured leg was amputated, and then they brought her home. She was a gentle, limping presence all through my childhood. A very mild-natured dog, and only when I was in my twenties, long after her death, did I realise her name was because of her missing leg. She lived outside, slept on old blankets in the shed. One night, my parents brought her inside to sleep by the oil heater in the middle of winter, and I understood she was dying. There was some blood coming from her nose, or her mouth. In the morning she had been taken away and buried in the garden, and I sat on the floor before the heater in the blank space she had been.

~

My mother said that anything that had once been alive should go back into the soil. Food scraps went into the compost, of course, including meat and bones, despite the general advice against this. Paper, torn into strips to allow air and microbes to move freely through. She would cut old pure cotton or silk or woollen clothes into small shreds and compost them too. Fish bones and flesh. Linen tea towels. She reluctantly left out larger pieces of wood, but longed for a woodchipper. She left cane furniture to rot and then buried it. She quoted a Buckingham Palace gardener she had once seen on television, who added leather boots to his compost bin. All that was needed was time, and nature. Anything that had lived could make itself useful, become nourishment in death, my mother said.

I never knew anyone else who had her reverence for the earth itself.

ACKNOWLEDGEMENTS

Thank you to Alison Mackay and Richard Morecroft, Alison Manning, Lucy Culliton, Susie and Craig Mitchell, Leslie Solar, Professor Jakelin Troy, Prue Sargent, Ailsa Piper, Vicki Hastrich, Lucinda Holdforth, Tegan Bennett Daylight. I'm grateful to Camilla Nelson and to the Copyright Agency for funding my residency at the University of Notre Dame in 2019–2020. My thanks to Ali Lavau, Christa Munns and Peri Wilson at Allen & Unwin, to Federico Andornino at Sceptre and Sara Schindler at Kein & Aber. Special thanks to Jenny Darling and Jane Palfreyman for guidance always, and their extreme kindness during 2022. Love and thanks to my brother and sisters for their trust and constant support. Last and always, my thanks to Sean McElvogue, for everything.

CREDITS

p. xi Epigraph: Nick Cave and Sean O'Hagan, *Faith, Hope and Carnage*, Text Publishing, 2022. Reproduced with permission.

p. xiii Epigraph: Elizabeth Hardwick, *Sleepless Nights*, Faber and Faber Ltd., 2019. Reproduced with permission.

p. 49 'What is most striking for me today', Zuzana Justman, 'My Terezín Diary', *The New Yorker*, 16 September 2019.

p. 105 David Gulpilil, *My Name is Gulpilil*, director Molly Reynolds, Vertigo Productions, 2021.

p. 121 Gustavus Hindman Miller, *10,000 Dreams Interpreted*, Hubbard Press, Northbrook Illinois, 1931.

p. 161 Simone Weil, *Gravity and Grace*, Routledge Classics, Taylor & Francis, 2002.

p. 165 'for the kingdom to be well', remarks spoken by Wynton Marsalis in *Jazz*, director Ken Burns, PBS, 2001.

p. 177 Elie Wiesel, *All Rivers Run to the Sea: Memoirs*, Schocken, 1996.

More praise for *The Weekend*

'Sharp, funny, beautiful.'

—HELEN GARNER, author of *Everywhere I Look*

'The most lovingly precise and insightful and funny and sad examination of female friendship . . . She has absolutely nailed it. It's a great, great book.'

—ANNABEL CRABB, host of *Chat 10 Looks 3* and *Future Women*

'An insightful, poignant, and fiercely honest novel about female friendship and female aging.'

—SIGRID NUNEZ, National Book Award-winning author of
The Friend

'Authentic, funny, brutally well-observed . . . As with the novels of Elizabeth Strout or Anne Tyler, these are characters not written to please, but to feel true.'

—*Sunday Times*

'Magnificent . . . *The Natural Way of Things* was a knife; *The Weekend* is a scalpel . . . Our epidemic of loneliness, growing class inequality, ever-present misogyny, male fragility, and the vicious rift of intergenerational animus . . . *The Weekend* achieves a faultless cultural vivisection. Wood's writing is at its incisively savage best . . . it's a privilege to have a front-row seat.'

—BEEJAY SILCOX, *Weekend Australian*

'Wood is a superlative stylist and storyteller . . . Themes touching on mortality, relationships and lives well- or ill-spent are canvassed with Wood's characteristic intelligence and passion. *The Weekend* is a quiet, devastating masterpiece.'

—THUY ON, *The Big Issue*

'*The Weekend* positively hums with life even as these three women are approaching the end of theirs. The book is exquisitely wrenching and poignant when dealing with female friendship and old age, yet it still manages to be funny and very real. I loved it.'

—CLAIRE FULLER, author of *Bitter Orange*

'Powerful, real and so urgent: *The Weekend* is an unforgettable study of friendship and loss. It's a delight to read such well-rounded older characters who are allowed to be angry, kind and purposeful, and still with human desires beyond not wanting to die. Brilliant: I loved it.'

—CAROLINE HULSE, author of *The Adults*

'With her deft sense for the cultural moment, Wood investigates the relationship between three women in their seventies, clearing out the holiday house belonging to a fourth friend who has recently died. As a meditation on ageing, friendship, class and gender, *The Weekend* is tender, tough-minded and assured.'

—*Australian*

'*The Weekend* is an unflinchingly observed celebration of the profundity and mundanity of friendship, treated with elegance, wit, and tenderness.'

—KIRAN MILLWOOD HARGRAVE, author of *The Mercies*

'I found reading *The Weekend* both hypnotic and profoundly unsettling. The prose is sharply vivid and precise, the characters and location exceptionally real and I challenge anyone to write a better description of an elderly dog and its owner. Masterful.'

—ROSAMUND LUPTON, author of *Three Hours*

'So good on ageing and on the fraught, warm friendships between women.'

—TESSA HADLEY, author of *The Past*

'Fierce and unsparing, angry and tender. I loved this story of three women in their 70s and their complex, endlessly critical but unconditional friendship.'

—JULIE COHEN, author of *Together*

'Rich with character and nuance, *The Weekend* reminds us all that life doesn't stop—whatever our age. A masterpiece of women's fiction like nothing I've ever read.'

—CHRISTINA DALCHER, author of *Vox*

'A visceral, arresting portrayal of friendship and grief . . . Wood tackles age sharply and movingly, and makes you consider the darker aspects of your own friendships.'

—*Press Association*

'Compassionate, funny and chock-full of painfully acute observations of compromise, friendship ageing and marriage (in all its forms), *The Weekend* is one of those deceptively compact novels that continues to open doors in your mind long after the last page.'

—PATRICK GALE, author of *Take Nothing With You*

'There's a feast of ideas for friends and book clubs to discuss . . . *The Big Chill* with a dash of *Big Little Lies* and an echo of Atwood's *The Robber Bride* . . . *The Weekend* is a novel about decluttering and real estate, about the geometry of friendship, about sexual politics, and about how we change, survive and ultimately die. Wood has captured the zeitgeist again, with a mature ease that entertains even as it nudges our prejudices.'

—SUSAN WYNDHAM, *Guardian*

'Mercilessly funny, cruel, empathetic, REAL dissection of three women in their 70s . . . can't stop reading.'

—VIV GROSKOP, author of *How to Own the Room*

'Wood handles the narrative with such empathy and dramatic dexterity . . . It's refreshing to read a novel that centres the experiences of older women with unflinching pathos and clarity. *The Weekend* is a sharply observed portrait of growing old that's sure to resonate.'

—*Books + Publishing*

'An expertly crafted novel . . . Wood's love letter to the importance of these families that we choose, cut through with her brilliantly acerbic wit. Sharply observed and excruciatingly funny, this is a celebration of tenderness and friendship that is nothing short of a masterpiece.'

—*Readings*

'Perhaps Wood's greatest achievement is her compassion for these flawed women, her thoughtfulness and her courage in telling this story. I do not know a woman over 40 who, while reading this book, has not wept for women and for themselves.'

—LAURA KROETSCH, *SA Advertiser*

'Wood's brand of social observation, honed in family drama *Animal People* and dystopian pre-#MeToo tale *The Natural Way of Things*, is in evidence here spare and unrelenting. But it also allows us to acknowledge exactly why we tolerate such tensions: it means we are there with, and for, each other.'

—*Vogue*

'One of the best novels of the year . . . I couldn't remember the last time I had reviewed a book like it . . . as beautifully contained as a stage play . . . Wood is able to maintain focus on her characters, which she dissects with the precision of a vivisector . . . [they] are scrutinised here without sentimentality, though not without humour. Wood is both comic and incisive in exploring the power dynamics and gaslighting that can take place in relationships . . . Wood is a writer who is majestically in control, making it easy for a reader to surrender.'

—MARIA TAKOLANDER, *Saturday Paper*

'Wood finds a beautiful balance between her three women, swivelling between their perspectives on the present and their shared past. The gaps between how a character sees themselves and how their friends see them are astutely drawn, both painfully comic and frequently heart-breaking . . . Wood is to be praised for taking female friendship seriously and for being caustically honest—there's not a sentimental line in this beautifully insightful book.'

—*Observer*

'*The Weekend* captivated me from the excellent opening chapter . . . Old female characters don't often get to occupy centre stage in modern fiction, but Australian author Charlotte Wood's three 70-something protagonists in *The Weekend* are exquisitely drawn . . . This wise, funny novel will help you understand yourself—and it may scare the s*** out of anyone brave enough to confront the truths within its masterful pages.'

—MARTIN CHILTON, *Independent*, Books of the Year

'Sharply observed and smartly paced . . . There's a steady crackle of irony from the gap between how the women judge each other and what they actually say . . . It might all seem a downward gear change from the violent feminist dystopia of Wood's previous novel, *The Natural Way of Things*, but don't be fooled. This is a stealthier book: smuggled into its tender but clear-eyed portrait of long-term friendship is a troubling and comfortless picture of old age as a loss of dignity that hits the sexes unequally.'

—*Daily Mail*